Consulting Editor
D. R. BROWNING
Principal Lecturer,
Department of Science,
Bristol Technical College (designated Bristol Polytechnic)

Mathematics
for Electrical and
Telecommunications Technicians

VOLUME 3

J. L. Smithson
Lecturer in charge of Mathematics
West Wythenshawe College of Further Education

McGRAW-HILL · LONDON
New York · Sydney · Toronto · Mexico · Johannesburg · Panama

Published by

McGRAW-HILL Publishing Company Limited

MAIDENHEAD · BERKSHIRE · ENGLAND

94243

Printed and bound by McGraw-Hill Far Eastern Publishers (S) Ltd. — Singapore

To
Geoffrey and Lesley

Preface

One of the many essential qualities of a good teacher is to know his students and to get close to them in speech and thought. If they do not understand his language of communication, no progress will be made until he understands theirs. Once this happy state is achieved, students will feel that they are moving forward *with* their teacher and not simply struggling to follow him.

It is in this spirit that this book was written—with the difficulties of the student in mind. If the expression of a rule or formula has been repeated at several points in the book, this is good class-teaching technique; diagrams have received the same treatment. It is not good practice to refer to a diagram several pages previously; a new principle deserves its own diagram if one is required.

The scope of the work covers the requirements of the syllabuses in mathematics for the Electrical Engineering Technician courses of several examining boards and the Telecommunication Technician courses of the C.G.L.I., the latter being a four-year course. The plan of this book takes into account the recently revised syllabuses of the City and Guilds of London Institute in respect of their Technician courses. I record with thanks, their co-operation in allowing me to use an advance copy of their publication. Students in Mechanical Engineering Technician, General Engineering, and O.N.C. courses will find the theory and many of the exercises in the book equally suitable for their syllabuses.

I have taught mathematics for thirty years in Technical and Grammar Schools and in Colleges of Further Education and this experience enables me to understand the academic background of the students for whom these books have been prepared. There are many worthy students in these courses who may have neglected their studies at school and who now realize the need for a mathematical understanding of their chosen vocation. With this in mind, the material has been developed from the very modest level of fractions and decimals in order to give every student the opportunity of a fresh start. The text is presented in detail and each step of calculations included; assumption of previous knowledge of a topic has been kept to an absolute minimum.

I have considered it useful to present the study of algebra as a topic which will be new to many students. In Vol. 1, a very close parallel is drawn between the numerical values of arithmetic and the letters, symbols, and signs of algebra. Much importance is attached to the consideration of the processes which link together the various terms, factors, and expressions in algebra—a necessary analysis in the important subject of transposition of formulae.

Similar treatment of other subjects such as indices, logarithms, functions, trigonometry, and calculus, should enable students to learn successfully from these three volumes. The numerous exercises to be worked, have been carefully chosen so that students can practise new principles on simple questions, thereby acquiring a feeling of confidence before approaching the more difficult problems.

The ever-present quadratic equation has received adequate treatment in Vol. 2 over 10 pages. At all points, I have endeavoured to show the links connecting previous study with new work, how the sine function of simple trigonometry leads to period, frequency, and angular velocity; how the sine and cosine rules and Pythagoras' theorem assist the compounding of vectors; and how the progression of accuracy from the mid-ordinate rule to Simpson's rule and integration for areas applies to the computation of average and r.m.s. values. The development and use of the constant 'e' deserves its early position and full discussion as a sequel to a general discussion of 'Growth' in chapter 1 of Vol. 3. The same volume introduces the calculus on a basis of understanding and application rather than rigorous mathematical proof, which belongs to a later period of a student's development. Chapter 10 shows the complex number as another language of communication in the expression of data in vectorial problems.

Acknowledgement is due to the examination boards listed below for permission to use questions from their examination papers; the accuracy of the answers to these questions is my responsibility.

City and Guilds of London Institute	C.G.L.I.
East Midland Educational Union	E.M.E.U.
Northern Counties Technical Examinations Council	N.C.T.E.C.

Union of Lancashire and Cheshire Institutes   U.L.C.I.
Yorkshire Council for Further Education   Y.C.

I am indebted to British Thornton Ltd., Manchester, for permission to use material from their instructional handbook on the Slide Rule. The section on Desk Calculators was written by Mr. L. R. Anderson, the Educational Adviser of Addo Ltd.; I am grateful for his contribution. I have received much encouragement from colleagues in the Department of Electrical Engineering at West Wythenshawe College of Further Education and I am thankful for their advice.

I owe an immeasurable debt of gratitude to my colleague of many years, J. F. G. Bigland, B.Sc. of Ilkley, for his patience and diligence in reading and revising the manuscript and checking every calculation in the three volumes.

J. L. Smithson

Notes

(a) At a late stage in the preparation of these volumes, it was decided that all units should conform to the rationalized metric system, known as SI. This has involved several hundreds of alterations in text and exercises, and, while all necessary re-calculations have been checked, it is possible that a few errors have escaped notice.

Acknowledgement

I am particularly grateful to be able to use the extracts (see Vol. 1, pp. 97–103) from PD 5686 April 1967, *The use of SI Units*, which are reproduced by permission of the British Standards Institution, 2, Park Street, London W.1, from whom copies of the complete publication may be obtained. This edition is being revised, but the main substance of Appendices A, B, and C will remain unaltered.

(b) Volume 1 covers the work in mathematics of E.T.1, 1st Year Telecommunication Technicians (Practical Mathematics), and 1st Year of the new Electrical Installation Technicians course (C & G 451) on which the first examination will be held in 1970.

Volume 2 covers E.T.2, Mathematics A of the Telecommunication Technicians course and 2nd Year of the new Electrical Installation Technicians course (C & G 451).

Volume 3 covers E.T.3, Mathematics B and Mathematics C.

Contents

1. Series

1.1 Growth, decay, change

The boundaries of all branches of knowledge have been extended by men of enquiring mind seeking an answer to the question, 'what next?' They were not content to accept the existence of a static environment. Some pursued their researches into the historical past, others into the future; all were very conscious of the importance of change.

This chapter is introduced in this spirit in order to create an atmosphere which will encourage the student to analyse the behaviour of numbers and possibly reach the conclusion, 'if these quantities continue to behave in a pattern similar to their past, then I shall be able to predict their value in n stages from now'; the most important words being 'analyse' and 'pattern'.

'Nature', defined in the dictionary as 'the established or regular course of things', is rarely, if ever, haphazard. In the study of mathematics, we call the numbers 1, 2, 3, etc., the natural numbers—a title they may not deserve in the future. In plants and animals, we speak of natural growth; in this chapter we shall be concerned with the growth of numbers.

Consider the following series of values:

(a) 1, 3, 5, 7, ...

(b) 2, 6, 18, 54, ...

(c) $10, 10^2, 10^3, 10^4$, ...

(d) $1, \frac{1}{2}, \frac{1}{4}, \frac{1}{8}$, ...

(e) $1 + 5x + 10x^2 + 10x^3 + 5x^4 + x^5$

(f) $1 + 1 + \frac{1}{2} + \frac{1}{6} + \frac{1}{24} + \cdots$

In (a) to (d), the patterns are simple and it is not difficult to predict the following values. In (e) the existence of a pattern is obvious but the means of its construction are not and there is no suggestion of the pattern continuing. In (f), at first sight, there is no pattern, unless it is written as

$$1 + \frac{1}{1} + \frac{1}{1 \times 2} + \frac{1}{1 \times 2 \times 3} + \frac{1}{1 \times 2 \times 3 \times 4} + \cdots$$

We shall see later that this series leads to a particular value which can be justifiably termed a natural number and is closely connected with the laws of natural growth.

1.2 Arithmetical progression (A.P.)

Any series whose terms are formed from the terms immediately preceding, by the addition or subtraction of a constant amount, is called an arithmetic progression or arithmetic series. For example, 1, 3 5, 7, ... is a series in which each term after the first is formed by the addition of 2 to the previous term. In general, we represent the series by S, where

$$S = a + (a + d) + (a + 2d) + (a + 3d) + \cdots$$

and $a = $ the first term

and $d = $ the common difference.

The first point of analysis is to relate the value of a term to its position in the series. Each term contains a and a varying number of d's; the 4th term, $a + 3d$, for example, contains a term in d whose coefficient, 3, is one less than the position number of the term. Before we accept this generalization, we must confirm whether this is true or not of other terms; we note that it is so. Hence the 14th term is $a + 13d$, and in general,

$$n\text{th term} = a + (n - 1)d \tag{1.1}$$

Sum of n terms of an A.P., i.e., S_n

$$S_n = a + (a + d) + (a + 2d) + \cdots + [a + (n - 1)d]$$

Rewrite the series in the reverse order:

$$S_n = [a + (n - 1)d] + [a + (n - 2)d] + \cdots + (a + d) + a$$

and add the two expressions for S_n.

$$S_n = a + (a + d) + \cdots + [a + (n - 1)d]$$

$$S_n = [a + (n - 1)d] + [a + (n - 2)d] + \cdots + a$$

$$\therefore 2S_n = [2a + (n - 1)d] + \left[\begin{array}{c} a + d \\ a + nd - 2d \end{array}\right] + \cdots + [2a + (n - 1)d]$$

$$= [2a + (n - 1)d] + [2a + (n - 1)d] + \cdots + [2a + (n - 1)d]$$

The result of addition of each pair of terms in columns on the right is $2a + (n - 1)d$. If the series has n terms, there will be n such totals. Hence

$$2S_n = n[2a + (n - 1)d]$$

$$S_n = \frac{n}{2}[2a + (n - 1)d] \qquad (1.2)$$

This, then, is the total sum of n terms of an A.P. Since the nth term is the last term, we can write $l = a + (n - 1)d$ and the sum of n terms is now

$$S_n = \frac{n}{2}[a + a + (n - 1)d]$$

$$= \frac{n}{2}(a + l) \qquad (1.3)$$

Of the terms used in (1.1), (1.2), and (1.3), n must be a positive integer, but S_n, a, d, and l may have any values; note that the common difference d is defined by

$$d = \text{any term} - \text{the preceding term}$$

Example 1.1. Given the series, 2, 6, 10, 14, ..., find (a) the value of the 15th term, and (b) the sum of the first 20 terms.

(a) 2, 6, 10, 14, ...

$a = 2, d = 4.$

$\therefore$ 15th term $= a + 14d$

$\qquad\qquad = 2 + 14 \times 4$

$\qquad\qquad = 58$

(b) $S_n = \dfrac{n}{2}[2a + (n - 1)d]$

$S_{20} = 10[4 + 19 \times 4]$

$\qquad = 800$

Example 1.2. The 8th term of an A.P. is -64 and the 3rd term is -4; find the series.

8th term, $a + 7d = -64$

3rd term, $a + 2d = -4$

$$\therefore\ 5d = -60, \quad \text{by subtraction}$$

$$\therefore\ \ d = -12$$

From $a + 2d = -4$, substituting for d, then $a = 20$. Hence the series is $20, 8, -4, -16, \ldots$.

Arithmetic means

A 'mean value' is a type of average, e.g., the mean value of 2 and 8 is $(2 + 8)/2$, i.e., 5. Hence the values 2, 5, 8, form an arithmetical progression. A series of arithmetical means are values lying between two given values so that the complete series forms an arithmetical progression.

Example 1.3. Insert 4 arithmetic means between the values 2 and 47.

The 4 arithmetic means lying between 2 and 47 make a series of 6 terms in A.P. Hence

6th term, $a + 5d = 47$

and $a \qquad\ = 2$

$$\therefore\ 5d = 45$$

$$\therefore\ \ d = 9$$

The four values required are therefore 11, 20, 29, and 38.

Example 1.4. The sum of an A.P. whose first term is 4 and whose common difference is 2, is 180. Calculate the number of terms in the series.

$$S_n = \frac{n}{2}\left[2a + (n - 1)d\right]$$

$$\therefore\ 180 = \frac{n}{2}\left[8 + (n - 1)2\right]$$

$$\therefore\ 360 = n\left[8 + 2n - 2\right]$$

$$= 8n + 2n^2 - 2n$$

$$= 2n^2 + 6n$$

$$\therefore\ 0 = n^2 + 3n - 180$$

$$= (n + 15)(n - 12)$$

$$\therefore\ n = -15 \text{ or } 12$$

The number of terms in the series is 12.

Figure 1.1 below, shows that the values expressed by an A.P. follow a linear variation.

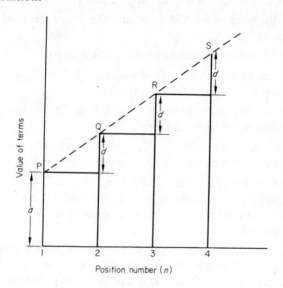

Fig. 1.1

The points P, Q, R, S, etc., would lie on a straight line, but it would be incorrect to join them as this would imply that we could read the values of terms at positions between 1 and 2, 2 and 3, etc., which is not valid since n must be a positive integer.

EXERCISE 1.1

1. Identify the A.P.'s in the following series and state their common differences.

   (a) $3, -2, -7, -12, \ldots$

   (b) $1.2, 1.6, 2.0, 2.4, \ldots$

   (c) $1, -1, 1, -1, \ldots$

   (d) $1, \frac{1}{2}, \frac{1}{3}, \frac{1}{4}, \ldots$

   (e) $(2a - b), (3a - 2b), (4a - 3b), \ldots$

   (f) $\dfrac{p}{q}, \dfrac{p + q}{q}, \dfrac{p + 2q}{q}, \ldots$

   (g) $0.1, 0.01, 0.001, \ldots$

   (h) $2, 2^2, 2^2 + 2, 2^3, 2^3 + 2, \ldots$

2. In those series of question 1 which are A.P.'s, find, (a) the 20th term, and (b) the sum of the first 12 terms.

3. The 5th term of an A.P. is 30 and the 11th term is 45. Find the series.

4. Insert 5 arithmetic means between -4 and -64.

5. The sum of the 5th and 7th terms of an A.P. is 32; the sum of the 3rd and 15th terms is 80. Find the series.

6. The sum of the first 10 terms of an A.P. is $77\frac{1}{2}$; the sum of the first 16 terms is 196. Find the series.

7. Given the series, $-101, -97, -93, \ldots$, calculate the position of the first term which has a positive value.

8. The equation of a straight line is $y = mx + c$. Three points on this line have x-co-ordinates a, b, and d respectively, forming an A.P. Prove that their y-co-ordinates also form an A.P. and state the common difference.

9. A coil is wound on a cylindrical former of 50 mm diameter with 100 layers of wire of diameter 0·6 mm. Assuming that the turns of each layer lie exactly on the top of the turns of the previous layer, and that there are 50 turns to a layer, calculate the total length of wire in the coil in metres. (Note; use the mean diameters of the turns.)

10. An athlete in training decides to run 100 km over a period of 10 days, increasing his distance daily by a constant amount. In the first 5 days, he has run a total of 30 km. Calculate the distance he runs on the 10th day to complete 100 km.

1.3   Geometrical progression (G.P.)

A series whose terms are formed from the terms immediately preceding by multiplication or division by a constant amount is called a geometrical progression or geometrical series.

In the series, 2, 6, 18, 54, $\ldots$, each term after the first is formed by multiplying the previous term by 3. It should be noted that the ratio (any term)/(preceding term) is constant throughout the series; this ratio is called the common ratio and denoted by r.

In general,

$$S = a + ar + ar^2 + ar^3 + \cdots$$

The 4th term is ar^3, and we note that the power of r is one less than the position number of the term and that this is true for all other terms.

Hence
$$n\text{th term} = ar^{n-1} \tag{1.4}$$

Sum of *n* terms of a G.P., S_n

Let
$$S_n = a + ar + ar^2 + \cdots + ar^{n-2} + ar^{n-1}$$

Multiply the series by r and write the terms on the right in correspond-ing columns of the powers of r.

From

$$S_n = a + ar + ar^2 + \cdots + ar^{n-2} + ar^{n-1}$$

$$rS_n = \quad\ ar + ar^2 + \cdots + ar^{n-2} + ar^{n-1} + ar^n$$

The pairs of terms in corresponding columns are now equal and by subtraction of the two series we obtain,

$$S_n - rS_n = a - ar^n \qquad \text{or} \qquad rS_n - S_n = ar^n - a$$

$$\therefore\ S_n(1 - r) = a(1 - r^n) \qquad\qquad \therefore\ S_n(r - 1) = a(r^n - 1)$$

$$\therefore\ S_n = \frac{a(1 - r^n)}{1 - r} \qquad\qquad\qquad \therefore\ S_n = \frac{a(r^n - 1)}{r - 1}$$

For convenience, the formula on the right is used when r is a value greater than 1; for all other values of r, we use the formula on the left.

Example 1.5. Given the series 3, 6, 12, 24, ..., find (a) the 10th term, (b) the sum of the first 10 terms.

(a) 3, 6, 12, 24, ...
$$a = 3 \quad \text{and} \quad r = 2$$

$$\therefore\ 10\text{th term} = ar^9 = 3 \times 2^9$$
$$= 3 \times 512$$
$$= 1536$$

(b)
$$S_n = \frac{a(r^n - 1)}{r - 1}$$

$$\therefore\ S_{10} = \frac{3(2^{10} - 1)}{2 - 1}$$

$$= \frac{3(1024 - 1)}{1}$$

$$= 3069$$

Example 1.6. Insert four geometrical means between 2 and 64.

The four geometrical means, along with the 2 and the 64 form a geometrical progression of 6 terms. Hence,

$$a = 2 \quad \text{and} \quad ar^5 = 64$$
$$\therefore r^5 = 32$$
$$\therefore r = 2$$

The required values are therefore, 4, 8, 16, 32.

Example 1.7. Given the series, $1, \frac{1}{2}, \frac{1}{4}, \frac{1}{8}, \ldots$, find the sum of (a) 5 terms, (b) 10 terms, (c) 15 terms.

(a)
$$S_n = \frac{a(1 - r^n)}{1 - r}$$

$$\therefore S_5 = \frac{1\left[1 - (\frac{1}{2})^5\right]}{1 - \frac{1}{2}} = \frac{(1 - \frac{1}{32})}{\frac{1}{2}}$$

$$= \frac{31}{32} \times \frac{2}{1}$$

$$= 1 \cdot 938$$

(b)
$$S_{10} = \frac{1\left[1 - (\frac{1}{2})^{10}\right]}{1 - \frac{1}{2}} = \frac{(1 - \frac{1}{1024})}{\frac{1}{2}}$$

$$= \frac{1023}{1024} \times \frac{2}{1}$$

$$= 1 \cdot 998$$

(c)
$$S_{15} = \frac{1\left[1 - (\frac{1}{2})^{15}\right]}{1 - \frac{1}{2}} = \frac{(1 - \frac{1}{32768})}{\frac{1}{2}}$$

$$= \frac{32767}{32768} \times \frac{2}{1}$$

$$= 1 \cdot 99994$$

Comparing S_5, S_{10}, and S_{15}, we note that although the values of the sums are increasing, the rise is becoming rapidly much less pronounced. The total for S_{15} suggests the question, 'how many more terms would be required for the sum to reach 2?'. The method shown below will answer this question without the labour of arithmetic.

Sum of an infinitely large number of terms of a G.P.

$$S_n = \frac{a(1 - r^n)}{1 - r} = \frac{a - ar^n}{1 - r}$$

$$= \frac{a}{1 - r} - \frac{ar^n}{1 - r}$$

Where r is less than 1, as in Example 1.7, then r^n is a fraction whose denominator increases with n. We have already seen that for $n = 15$, $r^n = \frac{1}{32768}$; it is left to the student's imagination to assess the value of r^{50}.

From $S_n = [a/(1 - r)] - [ar^n/(1 - r)]$, it can be seen that as n becomes very large, the term $ar^n/(1 - r)$ becomes extremely small and practically equal to zero. We say that S_n 'approaches the limit, $a/(1 - r)$', when the number of terms becomes infinitely large.

We write

$$S_\infty = \frac{a}{1 - r}$$

This argument can be applied only to those geometrical progressions where $r < 1$. Hence if $S = 1, \frac{1}{2}, \frac{1}{4}, \frac{1}{8}, \ldots$, then $S = a/(1 - r) = 2$. It would require an infinite number of terms for the sum to reach. 2.

Example 1.8. A mechanical application of A.P. and G.P.

A lathe is designed to accommodate work over a particular range of diameters. The speed at which it can be used will depend on the diameter of the work and the cutting speed of the material. The gear-box is designed to give suitable intermediate speeds and it can be shown that this distribution is best achieved by the terms of a G.P. rather than an A.P.

Cutting speed

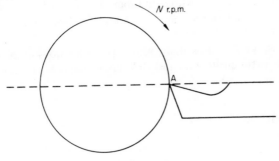

Fig. 1.2

A cutting speed of S m/sec means that a length of S m of the work piece passes the tool point A in 1 sec.

In one revolution of the work piece, a length πd m passes the point A. In N revolutions, this length will be $\pi N d$ m.

$$\therefore \; \pi N d = S$$

$$\therefore \; N = \frac{S}{\pi d}$$

Design an eight-speed gear-box for a lathe to suit 20 mm to 400 mm diameter work for a cutting speed of 0·5 m/s. Calculate the bar diameters for each speed and compare the results of using (a) A.P., and (b) G.P. distributions.

For 20 mm diameter, the highest speed is

$$N_8 = \frac{0\cdot5 \times 1000 \times 60}{\pi \times 20} = 477 \text{ rev/min}$$

For 400 mm diameter, the lowest speed is

$$N_1 = \frac{0\cdot5 \times 1000 \times 60}{\pi \times 400} = 24 \text{ rev/min}$$

(a) A.P.

Speeds:
$$N_1, N_2, N_3, \ldots, N_8$$
$$24, N_2, N_3, \ldots, 477$$
$$\therefore \; a + 7d = 477$$
$$\therefore \; a \qquad\quad = \underline{24}$$
$$\therefore \; 7d = 453$$
$$\therefore \quad d = 64\cdot7$$

The eight speeds will be 24, 89, 153, 218, 283, 348, 412, and 477 rev/min, correct to the nearest whole number. From $\pi N d = S$, we find the diameters for each of these speeds to be as follows: 398, 107, 62·3, 43·8, 33·8, 27·4, 23·1, and 20 mm.

We observe that this distribution provides no suitable speed for diameters between 400 mm and 107 mm, which is approximately three-quarters of the whole range.

(b) G.P.

Speeds:

$$N_1, N_2, N_3, \ldots, N_8$$
$$24, N_2, N_3, \ldots, 477$$

$$\therefore\ ar^7 = 477$$
$$\therefore\ a = 24$$
$$\therefore\ r^7 = \frac{477}{24} = 19\cdot9$$

No.	log
19·9	1·2989
$\sqrt[7]{19\cdot9}$	1·2989 ÷ 7
1·533	0·1856

$$\therefore\ r = 1\cdot533$$

The eight speeds will be 24, 24 × 1·533, 24 × 1·533^2, 24 × 1·533^3, ..., i.e., 24, 37, 57, 87, 133, 204, 312, and 478 rev/min. From $\pi Nd = S$, we find the diameters for each of these speeds to be as follows: 398, 258, 168, 110, 72, 47, 31, and 20 mm.

In practice it is found more useful to distribute the eight speeds according to a G.P., this giving a better choice of diameters, particularly of the higher values.

Example 1.9. A connection between A.P. and G.P.

If the variation of two quantities follows a law of the form, $y = Ak^x$, where A and k are constants, it can be shown that as the values of x vary according to an A.P., then the values of y will vary as the terms of a G.P.

A barometer reading atmospheric pressure takes mean sea-level as a base and pressure recorded then decreases as height above sea-level increases, according to a law of the form, $P = P_0 k^{-h}$, where P_0 and k are constants.

Let three successive values of h be h_1, h_2, and h_3 forming an A.P. Therefore,

$$h_2 - h_1 = h_3 - h_2$$

Let the corresponding values of P be P_1, P_2, and P_3. Therefore

$$P_1 = P_0 k^{-h_1}, \qquad P_2 = P_0 k^{-h_2}, \qquad P_3 = P_0 k^{-h_3}$$

Thus,

$$\frac{P_2}{P_1} = \frac{P_0 k^{-h_2}}{P_0 k^{-h_1}} = \frac{k^{-h_2}}{k^{-h_1}} = k^{h_1 - h_2}$$

and

$$\frac{P_3}{P_2} = \frac{P_0 k^{-h_3}}{P_0 k^{-h_2}} = \frac{k^{-h_3}}{k^{-h_2}} = k^{h_2 - h_3}$$

Since $h_2 - h_1 = h_3 - h_2$, then $h_1 - h_2 = h_2 - h_3$, and

$$\frac{P_2}{P_1} = \frac{P_3}{P_2}$$

This is the condition that P_1, P_2, and P_3 should be in geometrical progression.

Example 1.10. The atmospheric pressure at sea-level, 1000 m, and 2000 m is 1000, 950, and 902·5 millibars respectively. Calculate the pressure at 20,000 m above sea-level.

From Example 1.9, it is known that as the heights 0, 1000 m, and 2000 m form an A.P., then the corresponding pressures will form a G.P.

$$h \text{ (in A.P.):}\quad 0,\quad 1000,\ 2000,\ \ldots,\ 20,000$$
$$P \text{ (in G.P.):}\quad 1000,\quad 950,\ 902\!\cdot\!5,\ \ldots$$

The height of 20,000 m represents the 21st term of the A.P. We therefore require to find the 21st term of a G.P. whose first term is 1000 and whose common ratio is 0·95.

$$21\text{st term} = ar^{20}$$
$$= 1000 \times (0\!\cdot\!95)^{20}$$

No.	log
0·95	$\bar{1}\!\cdot\!9777$
	20
0·3581	$\bar{1}\!\cdot\!554$

$$= 358\!\cdot\!1$$

Therefore the pressure at 20,000 m is 358 millibars.

1.4 Compound interest

A sum of money deposited in an account with a bank, on which interest is paid, will increase in value year by year, by the addition of interest. If the interest is withdrawn each year, the deposit will remain constant; this is the condition of simple interest calculations. If the interest remains in the account, the deposit will grow and last year's interest will itself earn a small amount of interest this year: this is the condition of compound interest.

Let the deposit be £P at a rate of interest $R\%$ per annum. After interest is added at the end of the first year, the deposit will be, £$(P + RP/100)$, and this will be the amount which earns interest during the second year.

Hence, the amount at the end of the second year is

$$£\left(P + \frac{RP}{100}\right) + \frac{R}{100}\left(P + \frac{RP}{100}\right) = £\left(P + \frac{RP}{100}\right)\left(1 + \frac{R}{100}\right)$$

$$= £P\left(1 + \frac{R}{100}\right)\left(1 + \frac{R}{100}\right)$$

$$= £P\left(1 + \frac{R}{100}\right)^2$$

Note the correspondence between the 2nd year and the power 2 of the term $(1 + R/100)^2$.

At the end of the 3rd year, the amount $£P(1 + R/100)^2$ will become

$$£P\left(1 + \frac{R}{100}\right)^2 + \frac{R}{100} P\left(1 + \frac{R}{100}\right)^2 = £P\left(1 + \frac{R}{100}\right)^2\left(1 + \frac{R}{100}\right)$$

$$= £P\left(1 + \frac{R}{100}\right)^3$$

and we note the continued correspondence of the time period of 3 years with the 3rd power of the expression. It is therefore a reasonable conclusion to say that the amount A_n after n years is given by,

$$A_n = £P\left(1 + \frac{R}{100}\right)^n$$

Example 1.11. A sum of £100 is deposited at 5% p.a. compound interest; calculate its value after 5 years.

$$A_n = £100\left(1 + \frac{5}{100}\right)^5$$

$$= £100(1\cdot05)^5$$

No.	log
1·05	0·0212
	5
1·276	0·1060

$$= £100 \times 1\cdot276$$

$$= £127\cdot6$$

Example 1.12. In how many years, at 5% p.a. compound interest, will a sum of money double in value?

$$A_n = £P\left(1 + \frac{R}{100}\right)^n$$

$$\therefore\ 2P = P(1{\cdot}05)^n$$

$$\therefore\ 2 = 1{\cdot}05^n$$

$$\therefore\ \log_{10} 2 = n \times \log_{10} 1{\cdot}05$$

$$\therefore\ \frac{\log_{10} 2}{\log_{10} 1{\cdot}05} = n$$

$$\therefore\ \frac{0{\cdot}3010}{0{\cdot}0212} = n$$

No.	log
0·3010	$\bar{1}$·4786
0·0212	$\bar{2}$·3263
14·20	1·1523

$$\therefore\ n = 14{\cdot}2 \text{ years}$$

In Example 1.11 we have used a relatively small sum of money, £100; in a manufacturing or trading concern it would be insignificant. Very large sums of money, e.g., hundreds of thousands of pounds, would require a greater degree of accuracy than is provided by four-figure logarithms. A manufacturing company, requiring to buy machinery and other equipment and to provide for its replacement in x years' time, is not concerned with the calculation of interest earned by a bank deposit, but with the amount of money invested in the machine. This capital sum must not only earn sufficient week by week, but must provide also for depreciation, so that in x years' time, the machine can be scrapped and replaced with little or no loss. The calculation of depreciation follows the principles of compound interest and can be considered as a law of decay.

Example 1.13. Each year the capital value of a computer is reckoned to depreciate by 15% of its value at the beginning of that year. In how many years will its capital value be first below 10% of its original value?
                                                C.G.L.I. (part Qn.)

Modifying the compound interest law to allow for decreasing values, we apply,

$$A_n = £P\left(1 - \frac{R}{100}\right)^n$$

Let the original value of the computer be £V; then its value after n years will be £$(V/10)$.

Substituting the rate of depreciation for the rate of interest, R, then,

$$\frac{V}{10} = V\left(1 - \frac{15}{100}\right)^n$$

$$\therefore \ 0{\cdot}1 = (1 - 0{\cdot}15)^n$$

$$= 0{\cdot}85^n$$

Taking logarithms of both sides,

$$\log(0{\cdot}1) = n\log(0{\cdot}85)$$

$$\therefore \ \frac{\log(0{\cdot}1)}{\log(0{\cdot}85)} = n$$

$$\therefore \ \frac{\bar{1}}{\bar{1}{\cdot}9294} = n$$

$$\therefore \ \frac{-1}{-0{\cdot}0706} = n$$

$$\therefore \ 14{\cdot}16 = n \quad \text{(Reciprocal tables)}$$

Hence, in 15 complete years, the value of the computer will be less than 10% of its original value.

EXERCISE 1.2

1. Determine which of the following series form G.P.'s.

   (a) $3, 9, 15, 21, \ldots$

   (b) $3, 12, 48, 192, \ldots$

   (c) $\frac{1}{2}, \frac{1}{4}, \frac{1}{8}, \frac{1}{16}, \ldots$

   (d) $-5, 25, -125, 625, \ldots$

   (e) $\frac{a}{b}, \frac{b}{a}, \frac{b^3}{a^3}, \ldots$

   (f) $1, -1, 1, -1, \ldots$

   (g) $500, -100, 20, \ldots$

2. Of those series in question 1 which are G.P.'s, calculate (a) the 8th term, (b) the sum of the first eight terms.

3. Calculate the sum to infinity of the series, $3, 1, \frac{1}{3}, \frac{1}{9}, \ldots$.

4. Insert five geometric means between 3 and 192.

5. The difference between the sum of the first six terms and the sum of the first two terms of a G.P. whose common ratio is 2, is 6000. Find the series.

6. Design a six-speed gear-box for a lathe, to suit 10 mm to 250 mm diameter work for a cutting speed of 0·3 m/s. Distribute the speeds according to a G.P. and calculate the bar diameters for each speed.

7. Given the series, 3, 6, 12, 24, ..., state whether this is A.P. or G.P. Write down the logarithm of each term, and within the limits of accuracy of the logarithm tables, investigate whether they form a series. Prove your result in general terms.

8. The nine values of the resistances of an electric motor starter are in G.P. and range from 0·5 Ω to 2·5 Ω. Calculate the value of each step.

9. (a) Each year the capital value of a computer is reckoned to depreciate by 15% of its value at the beginning of that year. In how many years will its capital value be first below 10% of its original value?

   (b) State without proof the condition for the geometric progression $a + ar + ar^2 + \cdots$ to have a sum to infinity. Write down the recurring decimal $7\cdot4\dot5$ (i.e., 7·454545 ...) in terms of an infinite geometric progression and hence express it as a vulgar fraction.

   C.G.L.I. T.T.

10. The present number of telephone subscribers on a certain exchange is 3400 (nearest hundred) and the anticipated growth rate is 6% per annum (at 'compound interest law'). What is the likely number of subscribers ten years' hence. In how many years will the present number be doubled?

    C.G.L.I. T.T. (part Qn.)

11. A tape recorder uses a spool of tape, of outer and inner diameters 20 cm and 4 cm respectively. If the running speed of the tape is 18 cm/sec, and a complete spool runs for 45 min, calculate the length of tape on the spool and the approximate number of turns of tape on a full spool. Calculate the approximate thickness of the tape and the maximum and minimum angular velocities of the spool.

    C.G.L.I. T.T.

12. The tensions in the two sections of a belt passing round a pulley are given by $T = T_0 k^\theta$ where k is a constant and θ is the angle in radians through which the belt is in contact with the pulley. If T_0 is made constant, show that, as the values of θ increase in A.P., the values of T increase in G.P.

1.5 Binomial expansion

This is a very good example of the development of patterns which the student can observe for himself.

Any expression such as $(a + x)$ is called a binomial and we shall study the effects of raising the expression to successively higher powers.

$$(a + x)^0 = 1$$
$$(a + x)^1 = a^1 + x^1$$
$$(a + x)^2 = a^2 + 2ax + x^2$$
$$(a + x)^3 = a^3 + 3a^2x + 3ax^2 + x^3$$
$$(a + x)^4 = a^4 + 4a^3x + 6a^2x^2 + 4ax^3 + x^4$$

What generalizations can be made of the expressions on the right?

(a) Each consists of terms containing a and x; consider 1 as a^0x^0 and a^1 as a^1x^0, etc.

(b) The degree of the powers in each term in the same line is equal to the power of the binomial on the left.

(c) As the power of a diminishes, that of x increases.

(d) Each expansion on the right is exact, i.e., finite and complete, and contains one more term than the power of the binomial on the left.

What other feature remains to be discussed? The reason for the pattern of the coefficients is not immediately obvious; let us look at these without the a and the x.

$$(a + x)^0 = \quad\quad 1$$
$$(a + x)^1 = \quad\quad 1 \quad 1$$
$$(a + x)^2 = \quad\quad 1 \quad 2 \quad 1$$
$$(a + x)^3 = \quad\quad 1 \quad 3 \quad 3 \quad 1$$
$$(a + x)^4 = 1 \quad 4 \quad 6 \quad 4 \quad 1$$

The form in which these coefficients are set out is known as Pascal's triangle and any coefficient is made by the addition of the two coefficients astride it in the line above (see inset). We could very easily form $(a + x)^5$ in this way, but this method would become very slow and laborious if we required $(a + x)^{15}$.

Having discovered that a pattern exists, we should feel fairly certain that a more skilled way of arriving at an answer for any integral power of the binomial, can be found.

A simple guide offered to younger students when expanding $(a + b)(c + d)$, is that each term in the first bracket multiplies each term in the second bracket, i.e., we take all possible pairings. When we consider $(a + x)^n = (a + x)(a + x) \ldots$ to n factors, the pairings in the previous example will become groupings, and since we do not specify the value of n, we must make our choice of a's and x's very systematically.

First, choose all the a's for multiplication; result a^n. Next, choose all the a's except one, and in place of that one, choose an x; result $a^{n-1}x$. This choice can be made in more than one way; in fact in n ways since there are n brackets containing x; result, $na^{n-1}x$.

Third, we choose all the a's except two, and in place of those two we choose x's; result $a^{n-2}x^2$. Students without knowledge of permutations and combinations must now accept that there are $[n(n - 1)]/(1 \times 2)$ different ways of choosing 2 items from n items. Hence

$$(a + x)^n = a^n + na^{n-1}x + \frac{n(n - 1)}{1 \times 2} a^{n-2}x^2 + \cdots$$

from which it is not difficult to see that the next term will be

$$\frac{n(n - 1)(n - 2)}{1 \times 2 \times 3} a^{n-3}x^3$$

and that the last will be x^n.

The foregoing does not prove the binomial theorem, but establishes the manipulation of it on a basis of understanding and reasoning. By stating earlier that we should have n factors or brackets, we have assumed n to be a positive integer. Having established a pattern for any positive integral power of the binomial expression, we should investigate the possibility of writing down any term within the series without having to state all the terms preceding it; in other words, is the value of a term related to its position? Consider the construction of the 4th term,

$$\frac{n(n - 1)(n - 2)}{1 \times 2 \times 3} a^{n-3}x^3$$

There are three factors in the numerator, $n(n - 1)(n - 2)$
There are three factors in the denominator, $1 \times 2 \times 3$
The power of a is $(n - 3)$, the power of x is 3.

It would appear then that the 4th term is constructed by reference to a number which is 1 less than its position number; is this true for the other terms? This can be verified for the first three terms, giving firm justification for supposing that it will apply throughout the series. Hence the 7th term is

$$\frac{n(n-1)(n-2)(n-3)(n-4)(n-5)}{1 \times 2 \times 3 \times 4 \times 5 \times 6} a^{n-6} x^6$$

Validity of the binomial theorem

(a) If n is a positive integer, the series is finite and has $(n+1)$ terms; it is then true for all values of x.

(b) If n is a negative integer or a positive or negative fraction, then the series is true only if x is numerically less than a; in these conditions the series is infinite.

Standard form

A more easily handled form of the expansion is obtained if $a = 1$ (since $1^2 = 1^3 = 1^4 = \cdots = 1$). Thus

$$(1 + x)^n = 1 + nx + \frac{n(n-1)}{1 \times 2} x^2 + \frac{n(n-1)(n-2)}{1 \times 2 \times 3} x^3 + \cdots$$

In this form, the validity of the theorem is unaltered, except that condition (b) above now reads that x must be numerically less than 1.

Example 1.14. Expand $(1 + 2x)^7$ as far as the 4th term.

$$(1 + 2x)^7 = 1 + 7(2x) + \frac{7.6}{1.2}(2x)^2 + \frac{7.6.5}{1.2.3}(2x)^3 + \cdots$$

$$= 1 + 14x + 84x^2 + 280x^3 + \cdots$$

Example 1.15. Expand $(1 - x/2)^{-3}$ as far as the term in x^3.

$$\left(1 - \frac{x}{2}\right)^{-3} = 1 + (-3)\left(-\frac{x}{2}\right) + \frac{(-3)(-3-1)}{1 \times 2}\left(-\frac{x}{2}\right)^2$$

$$+ \frac{(-3)(-3-1)(-3-2)}{1 \times 2 \times 3}\left(-\frac{x}{2}\right)^3 + \cdots$$

$$= 1 + \frac{3x}{2} + \frac{3x^2}{2} + \frac{5x^3}{4} + \cdots$$

Approximations

If the series is infinite and we develop only the first few terms, then the degree of accuracy of the approximation becomes a point of consideration. In the following comparison, we shall write the coefficients as c_0, c_1, c_2, etc., simply as abbreviations and focus our attention on the behaviour of x.

(a) Expand $(1 + x)^{1/2}$ and evaluate if $x = 0.02$.

$$
\begin{aligned}
(1 + x)^{1/2} &= c_0 + c_1 x + c_2 x^2 + c_3 x^3 + \cdots \\
&= c_0 + c_1(0.02) + c_2(0.02)^2 + c_3(0.02)^3 + \cdots \\
&= c_0 + c_1(0.02) + c_2(0.0004) + c_3(0.000008) + \cdots
\end{aligned}
$$

at which point the series is correct to the 4th or 5th decimal place.

The coefficients c_0, c_1, c_2, etc., will clearly have some effect on the degree of accuracy reached in any term, but not to the same extent as the increasing power of the variable, x.

(b) Expand $(1 + x)^{1/2}$ and evaluate if $x = 0.6$.

$$(1 + x)^{1/2} = c_0 + c_1(0.6) + c_2(0.36) + c_3(0.216) + c_4(0.1296) + \cdots$$

at which point we have not established even the first decimal place. The conclusion is that a higher degree of accuracy is reached early in the series, the smaller we can make the value of x.

Example 1.16. Evaluate $1/\sqrt{4.08}$ correct to six places of decimals.

We must first express this quantity in the numerator of the fraction and write it in the form of a binomial expansion.

$$\frac{1}{\sqrt{4.08}} = (4.08)^{-1/2} = (4 + 0.08)^{-1/2}$$

Now write this last expression in the standard form of a binomial expansion.

$$(4 + 0.08)^{-1/2} = [4(1 + 0.02)]^{-1/2} = 4^{-1/2}(1 + 0.02)^{-1/2}$$

$$
\begin{aligned}
\therefore \quad \frac{1}{\sqrt{4.08}} &= \frac{1}{4^{1/2}}(1 + 0.02)^{-1/2} \\
&= \frac{1}{2}\left[1 + (-\tfrac{1}{2})(0.02) + \frac{(-\tfrac{1}{2})(-\tfrac{1}{2} - 1)}{1 \times 2}(0.02)^2\right] \\
&\quad + \frac{(-\tfrac{1}{2})(-\tfrac{1}{2} - 1)(-\tfrac{1}{2} - 2)}{1 \times 2 \times 3}(0.02)^3
\end{aligned}
$$

$$= \frac{1}{2}\left[1 - 0\cdot01 + \frac{3}{8}(0\cdot0004) - \frac{5}{16}(0\cdot000008) + \cdots\right]$$

$$= \frac{1}{2}[1 - 0\cdot01 + 0\cdot00015 - 0\cdot0000025 + \cdots]$$

$$= \frac{1}{2}[0\cdot9901475]$$

$$= 0\cdot4950738$$

$$= 0\cdot495074 \text{ correct to six places of decimals}$$

Example 1.17. The frequency of a tuned circuit is given by $f = 1/(2\pi\sqrt{LC})$. If the inductance increases by $0\cdot5\%$ and the capacitance remains constant, find the percentage change in frequency.

$$f_1 = \frac{1}{2\pi\sqrt{L_1 C}}$$

$$f_2 = \frac{1}{2\pi\sqrt{L_2 C}}$$

where $L_2 = L_1 + (0\cdot5/100)\,L_1 = L_1(1 + 0\cdot005)$. Therefore,

$$f_2 = \frac{1}{2\pi\sqrt{L_1(1 + 0\cdot005)C}}$$

$$= \frac{1}{2\pi\sqrt{L_1 C}\sqrt{(1 + 0\cdot005)}}$$

$$= \frac{1}{2\pi\sqrt{L_1 C}}(1 + 0\cdot005)^{-1/2}$$

$$= \frac{1}{2\pi\sqrt{L_1 C}}\left[1 + (-\tfrac{1}{2})(0\cdot005) + \cdots\right]$$

using only the first two terms of the binomial expansion. Therefore

$$f_2 = \frac{1}{2\pi\sqrt{L_1 C}} \times 0\cdot9975$$

$$= f_1 \times 0\cdot9975$$

The frequency is therefore diminished by $0\cdot25\%$.

Example 1.18. Under what conditions may the expression $(1 + x)^n$ in powers of x be used, if n is negative? Illustrate by the expansion of $1/\sqrt{1 + x}$. The current i in a microphone circuit at any instant t may be regarded as $i = v/(r_0 + r_1 \sin \omega t)$ where v, r_0, and r_1 are positive constants and r_1 is much smaller than r_0. Show that to a first approximation,

$$i = \frac{v}{r_0}\left(1 - \frac{r_1}{r_0}\sin \omega t\right)$$

$\begin{bmatrix}\text{and that to a second approximation the amplitude of the second} \\ \text{harmonic distortion present in the microphone circuit is } 50r_1/r_0\% \text{ of} \\ \text{the amplitude of the fundamental.}\end{bmatrix}$

C.G.L.I. T.T.

(The latter part of the question, in parentheses, is deferred to chapter 9, p. 181.)

The expansion of $(1 + x)^n$ in powers of x is valid only if $-1 < x < 1$, when n is negative.

$$\frac{1}{\sqrt{1 + x}} = (1 + x)^{-1/2} = 1 - \frac{1}{2}x + \frac{3}{8}x^2 - \frac{5x^3}{16} + \cdots$$

$$i = \frac{v}{r_0 + r_1 \sin \omega t}$$

$$= \frac{v}{r_0[1 + (r_1/r_0)\sin \omega t]}$$

The term $(r_1/r_0)\sin \omega t$ represents the x of the standard form of the binomial expansion. Since r_1 is much smaller than r_0, and the maximum value of $\sin \omega t$ is 1, then $(r_1/r_0)\sin \omega t$ is less than 1 and therefore meets the required condition for the expansion of a binomial expression with a negative power. A first approximation in the expanded form means that the second and higher powers of $(r_1/r_0)\sin \omega t$ are excluded. Therefore,

$$i = \frac{v}{r_0}\left(1 + \frac{r_1}{r_0}\sin \omega t\right)^{-1}$$

$$= \frac{v}{r_0}\left[1 + (-1)\frac{r_1}{r_0}\sin \omega t + \frac{(-1)(-1-1)}{1 \times 2}\left(\frac{r_1}{r_0}\sin \omega t\right)^2 + \cdots\right]$$

$$= \frac{v}{r_0}\left(1 - \frac{r_1}{r_0}\sin \omega t\right) \quad \text{to a first approximation}$$

EXERCISE 1.3

1. Expand $(1 + t)^{1/2}$ as far as the 4th term.
2. Expand $(1 - 2y)^{-2}$ as far as the 4th term.
3. Write down the 5th term of $(1 + x/2)^6$.
4. Write down the 6th term of $(1 + 2x)^{-1}$.
5. Expand $(4 + 3x)^{1/2}$ as far as the term in x^3.
6. Expand $1/\sqrt{9 - 3x}$ as far as the term in x^3.
7. Evaluate $\sqrt{108}$ by use of the binomial series, correct to four places of decimals.
8. Show that $\sqrt{2} = \sqrt{98}/7$ and hence use the binomial series to evaluate $\sqrt{2}$ correct to six places of decimals.
9. If x is sufficiently small that the terms in x^2 and higher powers can be neglected, write down approximations for $(1 + x)^{1/2}$ and $(1 - x)^{-1/2}$. Hence write down an approximation for

$$\sqrt{(1 + x)/(1 - x)}$$

   neglecting terms of the second and higher powers.

10. Expand $\dfrac{(8 - x)^{1/3}(4 + 2x)^{-2}}{(1 - x)}$, neglecting powers of x higher than the second.

11. A laboratory method of calculating the value of 'g' the gravitational constant, is by use of the simple pendulum. The length l and the time T of a complete swing are given by $T = 2\pi\sqrt{l/g}$; transform this to make g the subject. If the possible error in the measurement of l is $\pm 0.4\%$, and that in T, $\pm 0.2\%$, calculate by using the first two terms of a binomial series, the possible percentage error in g.

12. (a) Expand $(1 - x)^{1/2}$ in ascending powers of x as far as the term in x^4. What is the coefficient of x^r in the expansion? What restriction must be placed on the value of x for the expansion to be correct? Use it to evaluate $\sqrt{3}$ to four significant figures.

   (b) If the coefficients of x, x^2, x^3 in the expansion of $(1 + x)^n$ form an arithmetical progression, show that $n^2 - 9n + 14 = 0$.
   C.G.L.I. T.T.

13. (a) Expand $1/\sqrt{1 + x}$ in powers of x as far as the term in x^3, and suggest a suitable form for the general term of this expansion. What limitations must be placed on the value of x?

(b) In a 50 MHz oscillator circuit, the inductance L increases by 60 parts in 10^6, while the capacitance falls by 40 parts in 10^6, for every degree centigrade rise in temperature. Calculate to the nearest degree the change in temperature which will produce a 200 Hz change in frequency. Assume the oscillator frequency to be inversely proportional to $\sqrt{LC}$, and state clearly each step of your argument.

C.G.L.I. T.T.

14. The frequency of an oscillator can be obtained from the formula $f = k/\sqrt{CR}$ where k is a constant. If C is measured with a possible error of $\pm 0.4\%$ and R with $\pm 0.6\%$, calculate the possible percentage error in f.

2. The constant 'e'

2.1 Development of 'e'

In using tables of logarithms, students will have noticed that most books contain two distinct sets of logarithms; those in general use are called common logarithms, and the others 'Natural or Naperian or Hyperbolic logarithms'. Common logarithms are constructed on a base of 10, natural logarithms on a base whose symbol is 'e', having an approximate value, 2·718. The reaction of most students to this information is to say, 'why ever choose such an awkward number as 2·718 as a base?' It is useful that this question should arise in the early stages of this work and it is important that students should realize the fallacy in their question. The value of 'e' was not chosen, it occurs naturally; the value of π, 3·14159 approximately, was not chosen; it too occurs naturally as the ratio of the circumference of a circle to its diameter. The development of the constant 'e' shows that it is an essential constant in many processes of growth and decay.

Suppose that £1 is lent out at 4% compound interest per annum. It has been shown in chapter 1 that the deposit or principal of £1 grows each year as interest is added; but why only each year? This is often only an administrative convenience of accounting. Natural growth in plants, animals, chemical, and physical processes, does not take place in distinct amounts at the end of long periods, but is continuous over the whole period.

We shall develop the example of the growth of £1 by the accumulation of interest at more frequent intervals until we approach a state of continuous growth. This will be reached when the intervals between additions of interest become shorter and shorter, i.e., approach zero, which means that the number of occasions of addition become larger and larger, i.e., approach infinity.

It has been shown that $A_n = P(1 + R/100)^n$ for annual addition of interest. Therefore,

$$\text{Amount at the end of 1st year } = £1\left(1 + \frac{4}{100}\right)$$

$$= £(1 + 0{\cdot}04)$$

and   Amount at the end of 2nd year $= £(1 + 0{\cdot}04)^2$

If, however, the interest is to be added each month, the rate of interest will be $\frac{1}{12}$ of 4%. Therefore,

$$\text{Amount at the end of   1st month } = £\left(1 + \frac{0{\cdot}04}{12}\right)$$

and   Amount at the end of 2nd month $= £\left(1 + \frac{0{\cdot}04}{12}\right)^2$

and   Amount at the end of 12th month $= £\left(1 + \frac{0{\cdot}04}{12}\right)^{12}$

We now compare the yearly addition of interest with the monthly addition at the end of one year.

Yearly, $£(1 + 0{\cdot}04)$ $= £1{\cdot}04$

Monthly, $£\left(1 + \dfrac{0{\cdot}04}{12}\right)^{12} = £1{\cdot}0407$ (by binomial theorem)

Let the interval of interest payments now be reduced to one day. The amount at the end of the 1st year is $£(1 + 0{\cdot}04/365)^{365}$ which is $£1{\cdot}0409$. Thus the increase in frequency of payment causes an increase in the amount, but it can be shown that there is a limit to which the final amount approaches. Consider the following numerical results of binomial expansions whose form is similar to the calculation of interest monthly or daily.

$$(1 + \tfrac{1}{2})^2 = 2{\cdot}25$$
$$(1 + \tfrac{1}{4})^4 = 2{\cdot}44140$$
$$(1 + 1/5)^5 = 2{\cdot}48832$$
$$(1 + 1/10)^{10} = 2{\cdot}593744$$
$$(1 + 1/100)^{100} = 2{\cdot}70483$$
$$(1 + 1/1000)^{1000} = 2{\cdot}717065$$

The binomial expressions are all of the form $(1 + 1/n)^n$. The values on the right are increasing, but it will be noticed that although the value of n has increased considerably in the last three examples, there is very little increase in the results. It can be shown that as n increases without limit, the value of $(1 + 1/n)^n$ increases and approaches a limit whose value is 2·7183, correct to four places of decimals. This value is given the symbol 'e' in honour of the Swiss mathematician Euler (1707 to 1783).

To prove this, apply the binomial expansion to $(1 + 1/n)^n$.

$$\left(1 + \frac{1}{n}\right)^n = 1 + n\left(\frac{1}{n}\right) + \frac{n(n-1)}{2!}\left(\frac{1}{n}\right)^2 + \frac{n(n-1)(n-2)}{3!}\left(\frac{1}{n}\right)^3 + \cdots$$

$$= 1 + 1 + \frac{\dfrac{n}{n}\left(\dfrac{n-1}{n}\right)}{2!} + \frac{\dfrac{n}{n}\left(\dfrac{n-1}{n}\right)\left(\dfrac{n-2}{n}\right)}{3!} + \cdots$$

$$= 1 + 1 + \frac{\left(1 - \dfrac{1}{n}\right)}{2!} + \frac{\left(1 - \dfrac{1}{n}\right)\left(1 - \dfrac{2}{n}\right)}{3!} + \cdots$$

$(2! = 2.1, 3! = 3.2.1,$ etc.$)$

Now suppose that the value of n is increased without limit; we write, let $n \rightarrow \infty$. This is comparable with calculating interest, say every minute, thus making the interval very small and growth practically continuous. The terms $1/n$, $2/n$, etc., will now become exceedingly small, practically equal to zero, and can be neglected. Hence

$$(1 + 1/n)^n = 1 + 1 + \frac{1}{2!} + \frac{1}{3!} + \frac{1}{4!} + \cdots$$

$$\therefore e = 1 + 1 + \frac{1}{1.2} + \frac{1}{1.2.3} + \cdots$$

Similarly it can be shown that,

$$e^x = 1 + x + \frac{x^2}{2!} + \frac{x^3}{3!} + \frac{x^4}{4!} + \cdots$$

which is known as the exponential series and is true for all values of x.

Example 2.1. Write out the series for e^{-2x} as far as the 4th term.

$$e^{-2x} = 1 + (-2x) + \frac{(-2x)^2}{2!} + \frac{(-2x)^3}{3!} + \cdots$$

$$= 1 - 2x + 2x^2 - 4x^3/3 + \cdots$$

Example 2.2. Evaluate $e^{0.02}$ correct to six places of decimals.

$$e^{0.02} = 1 + 0.02 + \frac{(0.02)^2}{2!} + \frac{(0.02)^3}{3!} + \cdots$$

$$= 1 + 0.02 + 0.0002 + 0.0000013 + \cdots$$

$$= 1.020201$$

Example 2.3. Given that x is so small that x^2 and higher powers of x can be neglected, find an approximation for,

$$\frac{e^{2x}}{(1 - x)^{1/2}}$$

$e^{2x} = 1 + 2x + \cdots$ and $(1 - x)^{-1/2} = 1 + \frac{1}{2}x + \cdots$. Therefore

$$\frac{e^{2x}}{(1 - x)^{1/2}} = e^{2x}(1 - x)^{-1/2} = (1 + 2x + \cdots)(1 + \tfrac{1}{2}x + \cdots)$$

$$= 1 + 5x/2$$

The degree of approximation is defined by the highest power of the variable retained in the answer. In Example 2.3 the answer is a 'first-order approximation'.

2.2   Natural logarithms; use of tables

The significant difference in the use of these tables compared with the tables of common logarithms, lies with the characteristic, i.e., the integral part of the logarithm. In common logarithms it is not difficult to see that 257 lies between 10^2 and 10^3, and therefore the characteristic of its logarithm is 2. In using tables of natural logarithms it is not possible to visualize the value of n for which $2.718^n = 257$. The important point then, concerning the use of tables of natural logarithms, is that the characteristic is printed at the beginning of each line of logarithms; second, in contrast with common logarithms, there is no simple relation between $\log_e 257$ and $\log_e 25.7$.

Construction of tables

In the main table opposite, the extreme left-hand column contains numbers between 1 and 10, showing the decimal point and the figure in the first decimal place; the columns headed 0 to 9, and difference columns 1 to 9, contain the figures for the second and third decimal places of the number, respectively.

	0	1	2	3	4	5	6	7	8	9	Mean differences		
											1 2 3	4 5 6	7 8 9
1·0													
1·1													
1·2													
1·3								3148				30	
1·4													
⋮													
6·5													
6·6													
6·7	1·9021		9051									7	
6·8													
6·9													

LOGARITHMS OF 10^{+n} AND 10^{-n}

n	1	2	3	4 ...
$\log_e 10^n$	2·3026	4·6052	6·9078	
$\log_e 10^{-n}$	$\bar{3}$·6974	$\bar{5}$·3948	$\bar{7}$·0922	

Hence $\qquad\qquad \log_e 1·374 = 0·3178$

and $\qquad\qquad \log_e 6·725 = 1·9058$

For numbers less than 1 or greater than 10, we must make use of the subsidiary tables for 10^{-n} and 10^{+n}. The numbers whose logarithms are required must first be written in standard form, thus bringing them within the range of the left-hand column of the main table.

Example 2.4. Read $\log_e 0·01374$.

$$\begin{aligned}
\log_e 0·01374 &= \log_e (1·374 \times 10^{-2}) \\
&= \log_e 1·374 + \log_e 10^{-2} \\
&= 0·3178 + \bar{5}·3948 \\
&= \bar{5}·7126
\end{aligned}$$

Example 2.5. Read $\log_e 672 \cdot 5$.

$$\log_e 672 \cdot 5 = \log_e (6 \cdot 725 \times 10^2)$$
$$= \log_e 6 \cdot 725 + \log_e 10^2$$
$$= 1 \cdot 9058 + 4 \cdot 6052$$
$$= 6 \cdot 5110$$

Tables of anti-logarithms are not printed; we must reverse the procedure of Examples 2.4 and 2.5.

Example 2.6. If $\log_e N = 2 \cdot 6204$, find the value of N.

Since the largest value of a logarithm in the main table is $2 \cdot 3026$, we must adjust the given logarithm below this value by use of the subsidiary table for $\log_e 10^{+n}$.

$$\log_e N = 2 \cdot 6204$$
$$= 2 \cdot 3026 + 0 \cdot 3178$$
$$= \log_e 10^1 + \log_e 1 \cdot 374$$
$$= \log_e (10 \times 1 \cdot 374)$$
$$= \log_e (13 \cdot 74)$$
$$N = 13 \cdot 74$$

Example 2.7. If $\log_e M = \bar{6} \cdot 9980$, find the value of M.

Since only logarithms with positive characteristics are printed in the main table, we must adjust the given logarithm until it has a positive characteristic, again by use of the subsidiary table, $\log_e 10^{+n}$.

$$\log_e M = \bar{6} \cdot 9980$$
$$= (\bar{6} \cdot 9980 + 6 \cdot 9078) - 6 \cdot 9078$$
$$= 1 \cdot 9058 - 6 \cdot 9078$$
$$= \log_e 6 \cdot 725 - \log_e 10^3$$
$$= \log_e \left(\frac{6 \cdot 725}{10^3} \right)$$
$$\therefore M = 0 \cdot 006725$$

Note. It is usual at this stage in the study of mathematics, to adopt the convention that all natural logarithms are printed without the suffix 'e', but any other base must be shown; thus log 2 means the natural logarithm of 2. A more recently introduced symbol is 'ln' for natural logarithms; thus ln 2 means log 2. The use of 'ln' could cause some confusion with algebraic symbols and consequently has not been adopted in this book.

2.3 Conversion of logarithms to a different base

The most important conversion is from base 'e' to base 10 or vice versa.

Let $\log N = x$ ($\therefore N = e^x$) and let $\log_{10} N = y$ ($\therefore N = 10^y$). Thus

$$e^x = 10^y$$

Taking logarithms to base 'e' of both sides of the equation,

$$x \log_e e = y \log_e 10$$
$$\therefore x = y \log_e 10 \quad \text{since } \log_e e = 1$$
$$\therefore \log_e N = \log_{10} N \times \log_e 10$$
$$= \log_{10} N \times 2{\cdot}3026$$

This formula is sufficient whichever conversion is required.

2.4 Graphs of exponential and logarithmic functions

(a) $y = e^x$. The law of exponential growth
It is usual to print tables of the values of e^x and e^{-x} for values of x from 0 to 5 or 6 for two significant figures over most of the range. From these tables, the following values are sufficient to plot the graph of $y = e^x$.

x:	$-1{\cdot}0$	0	0·5	1·0	1·5	2·0	2·5	3·0
$y = e^x$:	0·4	1	1·6	2·7	4·5	7·4	12·0	20·0

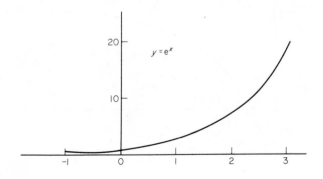

Fig. 2.1

(b) $y = e^{-x}$. The law of exponential decay

x:	-3.0	-2.5	-2.0	-1.5	-1.0	-0.5	0	1.0
$y = e^{-x}$:	20.0	12.0	7.4	4.5	2.7	1.6	1	0.4

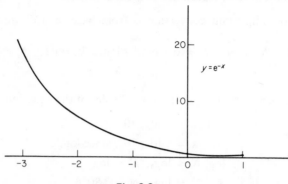

Fig. 2.2

We note the following points of importance in the two graphs.
  (i) each graph is continuous,
 (ii) e^x and e^{-x} are each positive for all values of x,
(iii) one graph is the mirror image of the other in the y-axis,
(iv) the gradient of e^x is positive and increases rapidly as x increases,
 (v) the gradient of e^{-x} is negative and decreases rapidly as x increases.

(c) $y = \log x$
The required values are read directly from tables of natural logarithms.

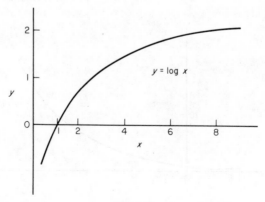

Fig. 2.3

The graph exists for positive values of x only. If $x > 1$, then y is positive; if $x < 1$, then y is negative. The gradient is positive and decreases as x increases. The graph of log x is the mirror image of $y = e^x$ in the line $y = x$ (Fig. 2.4 below).

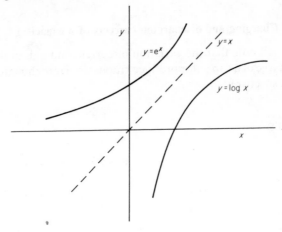

Fig. 2.4

(d) $y = 1 - e^{-x}$

It is often sufficient to sketch a graph from an analysis of its functional expression. As x increases, we have seen that e^{-x} decreases. In $y = 1 - e^{-x}$, we are therefore subtracting smaller and smaller values from 1; our result then must tend to approach 1.

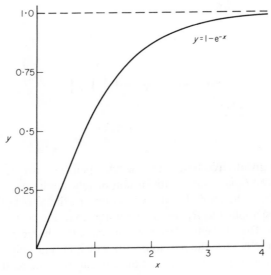

Fig. 2.5   Only positive values of x plotted

The value $y = 1$ is reached, in theory, when x is infinitely large; in practice, even when $x = 4$, $y = 0.98$. We could say that y reaches 98% of its final steady value when $x = 4$. The graph approaches the line $y = 1$ asymptotically.

2.5   Charging and discharging currents of a capacitor

We shall note that the variation of current and p.d. in the charge and discharge of a capacitor produce graphs similar to those in Figs. 2.2 and 2.5 respectively.

Charge

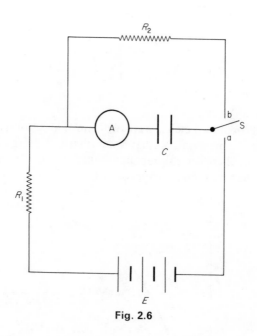

Fig. 2.6

In the given circuit with the switch open, no current flows and the capacitor C is assumed to be completely discharged, i.e., zero p.d. across it. When S is closed on position 'a', the whole of the voltage E must be applied to R_1; hence the initial charging current at time $t = 0$ is E/R_1. This charging current will increase the charge q on the capacitor and thereby raise the p.d. to v volts which in time will equal E. As the p.d. across C rises to E, so will the current from the battery decrease to zero and the capacitor will be fully charged.

The increase in p.d. across C and the decrease in current are given by,

$$i = \frac{E}{R_1} e^{-t/R_1 C} \quad \text{and} \quad v = E(1 - e^{-t/R_1 C})$$

where i and v are instantaneous values after time t sec. The mathematical proofs of these formulae will be given in a later chapter. The graphs of the two functions for i and v are shown in Fig. 2.7.

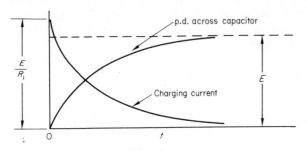

Fig. 2.7

Discharge

The switch S is now disconnected from 'a' and closed on position 'b'. The fully charged capacitor C will cause a current to flow through R_2, the ammeter A showing this current to be in the opposite direction to the previous charging current. The discharge current when $t = 0$, on closing S on 'b', will be a maximum value. As charge flows away from

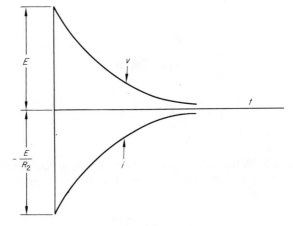

Fig. 2.8

C dissipated as heat in R_2, both current and p.d. across C will diminish to zero.

The instantaneous values of i and v on discharging are given by,

$$i = -\frac{E}{R_2} e^{-t/R_2C} \quad \text{and} \quad v = E e^{-t/R_2C}$$

the graphs of which are shown in Fig. 2.8.

Example 2.8. A capacitor of 12 µF is connected in series with a resistance of 0·7 MΩ across a 250 V d.c. supply. Calculate, (a) the initial charging current, (b) the p.d. across the capacitor after 4·2 sec (c) the current after 3 sec.

(a) Initial charging current $i = \dfrac{E}{R} e^{-t/RC}$

When $t = 0$, $\qquad i = \dfrac{E}{R} = \dfrac{250}{0·7 \times 10^6} = 357 \ \mu A$

(b) $v = E(1 - e^{-t/RC})$; $RC = 0·7 \times 10^6 \times 12 \times 10^{-6} = 8·4$

$$v = 250(1 - e^{-4·2/8·4})$$
$$= 250(1 - e^{-0·5})$$
$$= 250(1 - 0·6065)$$
$$= 250 \times 0·3935$$
$$= 98·4 \ V$$

(c) $i = \dfrac{E}{R} e^{-t/RC} = \dfrac{250}{0·7 \times 10^6} e^{-3/8·4}$

$$= \frac{250}{0·7 \times 10^6} e^{-1/2·8}$$

$$= \frac{250}{0·7 \times 10^6} e^{-0·3571}$$

$$= \frac{250}{0·7 \times 10^6} \times 0·7$$

$$= 250 \ \mu A$$

Example 2.9. A fully charged capacitor of 5 µF is discharged through a resistance of 0·4 MΩ. Find the time taken for the current to fall to 50% of its initial value.

$$i = \frac{E}{R} e^{-t/RC} \quad \text{(numerically)}$$

When $t = 0$, $\qquad i = \dfrac{E}{R} = $ initial current

When current falls to 50%,

$$\frac{E}{2R} = \frac{E}{R} e^{-t/RC}$$

$$\frac{1}{2} = e^{-t/(0\cdot4\times10^6\times5\times10^{-6})} = e^{-t/2}$$

$$\therefore \left(\frac{1}{2}\right)^2 = (e^{-t/2})^2$$

$$\therefore 0\cdot25 = e^{-t}$$

$$\therefore \frac{1}{0\cdot25} = \frac{1}{e^{-t}}$$

$$\therefore 4 = e^{t}$$

$$\therefore \log 4 = t \log e$$

$$\therefore 1\cdot39 \text{ sec} = t \quad \text{(since } \log e = 1)$$

Example 2.10. Evaluate $i = I_m e^{-Rt/L} \sin(2\pi ft + \phi)$ when $I_m = 50$, $R = 250$, $t = 0\cdot2$, $L = 15$, $f = 50$, and $\phi = \pi/3$.

$$i = I_m e^{-Rt/L} \sin(2\pi ft + \phi)$$

$$= 50\, e^{-(250\times0\cdot2)/15} \sin\left(2\pi \times 50 \times 0\cdot2 + \frac{\pi}{3}\right)$$

$$= 50\, e^{-10/3} \sin\left(20\pi + \frac{\pi}{3}\right)$$

$$= 50\, e^{-3\cdot33} \sin\frac{\pi}{3}$$

$$= \frac{50}{e^{3\cdot33}} \times \frac{\sqrt{3}}{2}$$

$$= \frac{50\sqrt{3}}{28 \times 2} \quad \text{(S.R.)}$$

$$= 1\cdot55 \quad \text{(S.R.)}$$

2.6   Growth of current in a circuit containing inductance

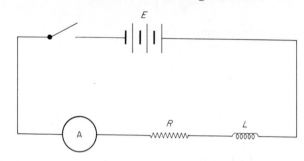

Fig. 2.9

The growth of current in the circuit is opposed by the e.m.f. induced in the coil of inductance L. The instantaneous current i amperes after a time t seconds is given by,

$$i = \frac{E}{R}(1 - e^{-Rt/L})$$

the proof of this being part of chapter 5. The graph of this function is shown below in Fig. 2.10. When t is large, then $e^{-Rt/L}$ is very small and $i = E/R$, which represents the final steady current I.

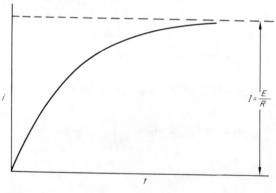

Fig. 2.10

2.7   Time constants

(a) Capacitive circuit

$$v = E(1 - e^{-t/CR})$$

As t increases, $e^{-t/CR}$ decreases; hence the p.d. across the capacitor increases. The time constant, T, of the circuit is defined as the time in which the p.d. across the capacitor would reach its final value if it continued to increase at its initial rate; this is shown by the tangent to the curve of p.d. in Fig. 2.11.

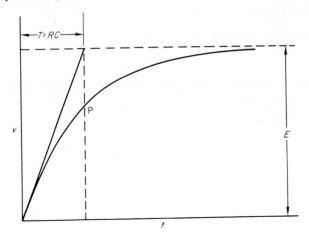

Fig. 2.11

This constant T can be shown to be equal to RC sec, in which time the actual p.d. across the capacitor is represented by position P in Fig. 2.11. Hence

$$v = E(1 - e^{-RC/RC}) = E(1 - e^{-1})$$
$$= E(1 - 0{\cdot}3679)$$
$$= 0{\cdot}6321E$$

The time constant is thus the time required for the p.d. across the capacitor to reach $63{\cdot}2\%$ of its final value.

From $i = (E/R)\, e^{-t/RC}$, the same consideration applied to the charging current, would show that at time $T = RC$ sec, the current has diminished to $36{\cdot}8\%$ of its original value.

(b) Inductive circuit

$$i = \frac{E}{R}(1 - e^{-Rt/L})$$

The time constant in an inductive circuit is given by $T = L/R$ sec. Hence, when $t = T = L/R$, then

$$i = \frac{E}{R}(1 - e^{-1}) = \frac{E}{R}(0{\cdot}6321)$$

The time constant is thus the time required for current to increase to 63·2% of its final steady value.

(c) Heating coil

In a heating coil, the temperature rise $\theta°C$, is given by,

$$\theta = \theta_f(1 - e^{-t/T})$$

where θ_f is the final steady temperature and T sec is the time constant of the coil.

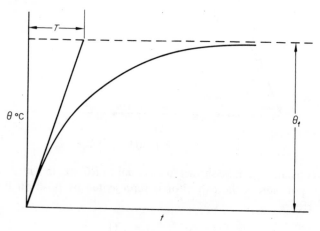

Fig. 2.12

The growth of temperature thus follows a similar pattern to the growth of current in an inductive circuit and of p.d. across a capacitor, the temperature reached in T sec being 63·2% of the final steady temperature. If the coil were allowed to cool, the temperature after t sec would be given by,

$$\theta = \theta_i e^{-t/T}$$

where θ_i is the initial temperature above the surrounding atmosphere. This function is analogous to the fall of p.d. on the discharge of a capacitor.

2.8   Determination of laws; graphs involving 'e'

It has been shown in Volume 2 that if two variables x and y are connected by a law of the form $y = ax^n$ then the application of logarithms produces a straight-line function from which we measure a and n from the corresponding graph.

We now consider a function of the type, $y = a\,e^{bx}$, from which we are required to find values of the constants a and b. There is one important point of similarity with the previous function in that n and b are powers; it is reasonable to assume therefore that the application of logarithms to the function $y = a\,e^{bx}$ will produce a similar linear function. There is an equally important point of contrast in that the variable x in $y = a\,e^{bx}$, is part of the power whereas in $y = ax^n$, it is the base of the power. Both functions are dealt with below for convenience of comparison.

$$y = ax^n$$

Taking logarithms to base 10,

$$\log_{10} y = \log_{10} a + \log_{10} (x^n)$$
$$= n \log_{10} x + \log_{10} a$$

Hence plot $\log_{10} y$ against $\log_{10} x$. Gradient $= n$; intercept $= \log_{10} a$.

$$y = a\,e^{bx}$$

Taking logarithms to base 10,

$$\log_{10} y = \log_{10} a + \log_{10} (e^{bx})$$
$$= bx \log_{10} e + \log_{10} a$$

To show a straight-line function more simply, let $B = b \log_{10} e$, then

$$\log_{10} y = Bx + \log_{10} a$$

Hence plot $\log_{10} y$ against x. Gradient $= B$; intercept $= \log_{10} a$. From the measured gradient of the graph, say $1\cdot3$, we find the constant b as follows.

$$B = 1\cdot3$$
$$\therefore\ b \log_{10} e = 1\cdot3$$
$$\therefore\ b = \frac{1\cdot3}{\log_{10} e} = \frac{1\cdot3}{0\cdot4343}$$

A more direct method for the function $y = a\,e^{bx}$ is obtained if we use natural logarithms.

$$y = a\,e^{bx}$$
$$\therefore\ \log y = \log a + bx \log e$$
$$= bx + \log a \quad (\text{since } \log e = 1)$$

Hence plot log y against x; the gradient is now a direct representation of the constant b.

Semi-logarithmic graph paper

Graph paper printed specially for use with this type of function has lengths on the vertical axis graduated in logarithmic values but numbered with ordinary integers, and lengths on the horizontal axis graduated in inches or centimetres; hence an alternative specification for this paper is 'log-linear'. The logarithmic scale is equally suitable for common logarithms or natural logarithms.

Example 2.11. The voltage v at any time t during the discharge of a capacitor is given by $v = E\,e^{-t/RC}$, which can be written in the form $v = E\,e^{-bt}$. The following observations of v and t were recorded.

t:	1	2	3	4	5	6
v:	164	134	110	89·9	73·6	60·2

By drawing a suitable straight-line graph, determine whether the observations follow a law of the form, $v = E\,e^{-bt}$, and find suitable values for E and b. What was the original p.d. across the capacitor? Find also the value of t when the p.d. has fallen to half its original value.

$$v = E\,e^{-bt}$$
$$\therefore\ \log v = \log E - bt \log e$$
$$= \log E - bt$$

We therefore plot log v against t, the measured gradient giving the numerical value of b and from the form of the last equation, we expect to find a negative gradient. The intercept will represent log E, from which we shall obtain E by reading the anti-logarithm, or directly if we use semi-logarithmic paper. The gradient is represented geometrically by AB/BC, but since the vertical and horizontal axes are not graduated with the same scales, we are not able to use the actual lengths of AB and BC. Hence

$$\text{Gradient} = \frac{\log v_1 - \log v_2}{t_1 - t_2} = \frac{\log 165 - \log 74}{1 - 5}$$
$$= -0{\cdot}2$$

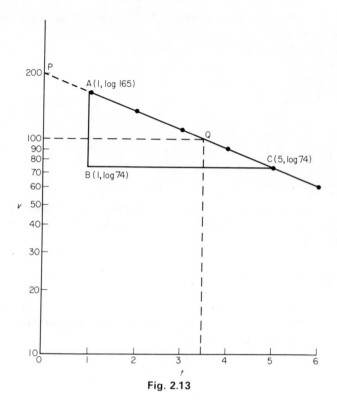

Fig. 2.13

Intercept read at P, since $t = 0$, gives $E = 200$ V. This value of E also represents the original value of the p.d. across the capacitor. The position Q on the graph shows $t = 3.5$ sec when the p.d. has fallen to half its original value.

The observations thus verify a law of the form,

$$v = 200\ e^{-0.2t}$$

EXERCISE 2.1

1. Use tables to read the values of the following:

(a) $e^{1.37}$ (b) $e^{-3.45}$

(c) $1/e^{0.78}$ (d) $1/e^{-0.56}$

(e) $\log 2.759$ (f) $\log 45.81$

(g) $\log 0.007523$ (h) $\log 1000$

(i) $\log 8.432$ (j) $\log 678.3$

(k) $\log 0.2718$ (l) $\log (1/100)$

2. If the following values represent log N, find the corresponding values of N:

(a) 1·7568   (b) 3·0089
(c) $\bar{1}$·2381   (d) $\bar{4}$·7052
(e) 7·0426   (f) $\bar{2}$·3026
(g) 5·3948   (h) $\bar{1}$·0000

3. Solve the following equations to find the values of x:

(a) $e^x = 12\cdot86$ (b) $e^{-x} = 0\cdot3642$
(c) $e^{2x} = 45\cdot56$ (d) $10\,e^{-3x} = 2\cdot5$
(e) $1 - e^{-2x} = 0\cdot5$ (f) $\frac{5}{2}\,e^{0\cdot25x} = 5\cdot6$
(g) $\sqrt{e^x} = 4\cdot8$ (h) $e^{1/x} = 27\cdot5$

4. The tensions in the two sides of a belt passing round a pulley are given by $T_1 = T_2\,e^{\mu\theta}$ where μ is the coefficient of friction and θ is the angle of lap in radians. If $T_2 = 18\cdot5$, $\mu = 0\cdot4$, and $\theta = \pi$ radians, calculate the value of T_1. Calculate also the value of θ which would make the ratio $T_1:T_2$ equal to 4:3, using the same value of $\mu = 0\cdot4$.

5. The current i amperes flowing in a circuit containing an inductance of L henrys in series with a resistance of R ohms, and a constant e.m.f. E volts, is given by,

$$i = \frac{E}{R}(1 - e^{-Rt/L})$$

Given $E = 240$ V, $R = 5\,\Omega$, $L = 6$ H, and $t = 2 \times 10^{-1}$ sec find the value of i.

6. The thermionic emission current from a metallic surface is given by

$$I = AT^2\,e^{-b/T}$$

Calculate the value of I if $T = 1500$, $b = 5 \times 10^4$, and $A = 4\cdot03 \times 10^6$.

7. The capacitance between two parallel wires is given by,

$$C = \frac{k}{\log\left[(d - r)/r\right]}$$

Calculate C if $k = 26\cdot2 \times 10^{-12}$, $d = 25$ cm, and $r = 0\cdot5$ cm.

8. A formula for the self-inductance of a cored wire is $L = k\log(d_2/d_1)$. Calculate the value of L if $k = 0\cdot09$, $d_2 = 0\cdot8$ cm, and $d_1 = 0\cdot6$ cm.

9. Calculate the value of θ from the formula $\theta = \theta_0\,e^{-bt}$ given that $\theta_0 = 100$, $b = 1\cdot2$, and $t = 4$.

10. The temperature rise in a coil which is being heated electrically is given by $\theta = \theta_f(1 - e^{-t/T})$. Calculate the value of θ_f, given that $\theta = 35$, $t = 60$, and $T = 50$.

11. (a) Write down the value of $\log_{10} 100$ and hence find $\log_e 100$.
    (b) Rewrite the equation $y = e^x$ in logarithmic form and find the value of x when $y = 50$.
    (c) The formula $y = A\,e^{-pt} \sin \theta$ gives the displacement of a body executing damped oscillations. Calculate the value of y when $A = 0.1$ m, $p = 0.6$, $t = 1$ sec, and $\theta = 30°$.   N.C.T.E.C.

12. (a) The current charging a capacitor is given by the formula,

$$i = \frac{E}{R} e^{-t/RC}$$

Find the value of i when $E = 15$, $R = 3 \times 10^3$, $t = 10^{-2}$, $C = 5 \times 10^{-6}$, and $e = 2.718$.
    (b) If $e = 1 - r^n$, find the value of e when $r = 0.46$ and $n = 1.2$.
                                                E.M.E.U.

13. A capacitor and a resistor are joined in series and connected to a d.c. supply. After a time t the current i flowing is given by $i = 10\,e^{-2t}$.

    Draw a graph of i (vertically) against t between $t = 0$ and $t = 1.2$ plotting the points at intervals of t equal to 0.2. State Simpson's rule and use it, taking six strips, to determine the area enclosed between the curve and the t-axis between $t = 0$ and $t = 1.2$. Give the answer correct to three significant figures.
                                                U.E.I.

14. Plot a graph to represent the equation $y = 4\,e^{-x^2/10}$ from $x = 0$ to $x = 4$. From your graph find, correct to the first decimal place, the solution of the equation,

$$x = 4\,e^{-x^2/10}$$
                                                E.M.E.U.

15. (a) Make a freehand sketch of the graph of the function $y = e^x$ indicating the essential features of the curve.
    (b) If $\log_e (65.2/y) = 1.4$, find the value of y.
                                                N.C.T.E.C.

16. (a) Given that $\log_a x = \log_b x / \log_b a$, use logarithms to base 10, to calculate, (i) $\log_e 8$, (ii) $\log_e \pi$.
    (b) An electric current i amp at any time t sec is given by the expression $i = 50\,e^{-10t}$. Calculate the value of i when $t = 0.2$ sec.
                                                U.L.C.I.

17. A system of n receivers is said to have a diversity gain of G decibels given by,

$$G = \frac{20}{m}\left(1 - \frac{1}{n}\right)\log_e\left(\frac{1}{k}\right)$$

where k is the proportion of time loss allowed, and m is a constant for the system.

    If $m = 2\cdot1$ when $n = 3$ and $k = 0\cdot2$, calculate G.

C.G.L.I. T.T. (part Qn.)

18. The formula $T_1 = T_2\, e^{\mu\theta\,\sec\alpha}$ connects the tensions T_1 and T_2 on the tight and slack sides of a rope passing round a pulley, where μ = the coefficient of friction, α = semi-angle of the groove, and θ radians equals the angle of lap. Calculate T_1 if $T_2 = 34\cdot7$, $\mu = \frac{1}{4}$, $\alpha = 22\frac{1}{2}°$, and $\theta = 2\pi/3$. Also express μ in terms of T_1, T_2, θ, and α.

C.G.L.I. T.T. (part Qn.)

19. Plot the function $y = e^{-x}\sin 2x$ (x in radians), from $x = 0$ to $x = \pi/2$ at intervals of $\pi/8$. Use Simpson's rule to evaluate the approximate area between the x-axis and the curve, and hence deduce the mean value of $e^{-x}\sin 2x$ from $x = 0$ to $x = \pi/2$.

C.G.L.I. T.T.

20. An uncharged capacitor (C) in series with a resistor (R) is connected to a constant voltage supply (V). Why does the voltage across the capacitor rise slowly?

    Write down an expression for the voltage across the capacitor after time t sec. Sketch a curve of voltage against time. What is the meaning of 'time constant' for the circuit?

    A capacitor of 10 µF is charged through a series resistor from a 100 V battery. What value of resistor will give a time constant of $0\cdot1$ sec? For this circuit, calculate the current flowing (a) at the instant of switching on, (b) after a time equal to the time constant, and (c) after a long period of time.

C.G.L.I. T.T. Princ. B.

21. A 10 V battery of negligible internal resistance is switched across a coil of 1 H inductance and 40 Ω resistance. Sketch a curve showing the current/time relationship from the instant of switching on. Write down an expression representing the instantaneous value of the current. Find (a) the initial current, and (b) the final current.

    If a second coil were wound over the first but insulated from it, what effect would occur in the second coil due to the increasing current in the first winding?

At what time relative to the switching-on of the battery would the effect in the second winding be a maximum? Give reasons for your answer. Assume that the terminals of the second coil are open-circuited throughout.

C.G.L.I. T.T. Princ. B.

22. A 10 μF capacitor in series with a 1 MΩ resistor is charged from a source giving a constant current of 1·0 mA. Illustrate, by means of a graph, for the range 0 to 100 V, how the voltage across the capacitor is related to the charging time.

Suppose now that the charging arrangements are altered so that a d.c. supply maintains 100 V across the RC series circuit. Write down an expression for the voltage across the capacitor t sec from switching on, assuming that the capacitor is initially uncharged. Illustrate the change in voltage with time by means of a graph.

What is the time constant for the circuit? What is the current (a) at the instant of switching on, (b) when the voltage across the capacitor is 100 V.

C.G.L.I. T.T. Princ. B.

EXERCISE 2.2

1. In a discharge test on a capacitor the following results were obtained for the discharge current i after a time t.

i:	26·5	21·2	17·3	14·4	11·5	9·5
t:	0	40	80	120	160	200

Plot suitable variables to show that the law relating i and t is of the form, $i = I_m e^{kt}$ and hence obtain the values of I_m and k.

U.E.I.

2. The tension T N in a belt passing round a pulley is related to the angle of lap θ radians by the formula $T = T_0 e^{\mu\theta}$, where T_0 and μ are constants. Verify graphically that the following observations satisfy a law of the form given and find approximate values of T_0 and μ.

θ:	1·0	1·5	2·0	2·5	3·0	3·5	4·0
T:	16·5	21·2	27·2	35·0	45·0	57·5	74·0

3. The following table records the temperature T (deg. C) of a piece of metal at time t (min).

t:	0	5	10	15	20
T:	493	445	401	363	328

Plot log T against t (the base of logarithms is left to the candidate's choice), and deduce the law connecting T and t. Give the law in a form free from logarithms and evaluate the constants involved. Find T, when $t = 12$, (a) from the formula, (b) from the graph.

U.E.I. S.III.

4. When a capacitor is being charged the p.d. across it, v volts, increases with the time t seconds according to $v = E(1 - e^{-kt})$ where E is the applied voltage and k is a constant. Given that E is 200 V, determine graphically whether the following observations satisfy this law and find an approximate value of k from your graph.

t:	0	1	2	3	4	5	6
v:	0	36·2	65·9	90·2	110	126	140

5. Atmospheric pressure decreases as height above sea-level increases, according to $P = P_0 e^{kh}$. Verify graphically that the following observations satisfy this law and from your graph find approximate values of the constants P_0 and k.

h:	1000	3000	5000	7000	9000	11,000
P:	29·0	27·2	25·2	23·4	21·8	20·4

6. The charge on a capacitor is leaking away and the p.d. between the plates was measured at minute intervals with results as follows;

t (min):	1	2	3	4	5
V (volts):	3·70	2·74	2·03	1·51	1·12

Show by plotting $\log_e V$ against t, that a straight line is produced, indicating that a law of the form $V = a\,e^{-bt}$ is satisfied.

From your graph find the value of $\log_e V$ when t is 0, and hence obtain the initial p.d. between the plates, and also find the time taken for the p.d. to fall to one-half of its initial value.

E.M.E.U.

7. The following observations were made of the current i amp at time t sec, in an inductive circuit

t:	0	0·01	0·02	0·03	0·04	0·05	0·06
i:	0	0·316	0·432	0·475	0·491	0·497	0·499

Write down an estimate for the value of the final steady current I. The observations are expected to follow a law of the form,

$i = I(1 - e^{-Rt/L})$. Using the estimated value of I, deduce that this is equivalent to the function,

$$\log(1 - 2i) = -\frac{Rt}{L}$$

and by drawing a suitable straight-line graph, find the value of R/L; hence write down the time constant of the circuit.

8. The population, in millions, of the United States is recorded as:

Year:	1790	1820	1840	1860	1880
Popln. (x):	3·2	7·9	14·8	26·9	43·4

Assuming an exponential law of growth, $x = a\,e^{kt}$, at a time t years after 1790, derive a straight-line graph, and from this graph, estimate the constants a and k. For what range of years is the assumption a reasonable one?

C.G.L.I. T.T.

9. Eighty batches of transistors are tested at regular intervals in a factory, and the number of 'rejects' in each batch tested is summarized below.

No. of rejects in a batch (x):	0	1	2	3	4
No. of batches in which they occur (y):	37	21	12	6	4

An exponential law of the type $y = a\,e^{-kx}$ is assumed to connect these measurements. By plotting suitable variables, show this assumption to be reasonable, and from the graph obtain estimates of the constants a and k.

C.G.L.I. T.T.

10. The following data was obtained in testing cement mixes having different values of the water/cement ratio.

Water/cement ratio (x):	0·4	0·5	0·6	0·7	0·8
Strength in MN/m² (y):	2·24	1·77	1·31	1·01	0·76

Show, by plotting suitable variables, that the formula $y = a\,e^{-kx}$ is a reasonable one for the range of x-values tested. Use the graph to obtain estimates of the constants a and k. Could the constant a have any physical significance?

C.G.L.I. T.T.

2.9   Transformation of formulae involving natural logarithms

We recall the definition of a logarithm as a power. If $\log_b N = x$, then $N = b^x$.

The first relation is described in a logarithmic form, the second in an exponential form, the base in each case being b. For purposes of numerical evaluation, students often prefer to use common logarithms in preference to natural logarithms, in which case they should be careful to specify this in their work.

Example 2.12. Given $i = \dfrac{E}{R}(1 - e^{-Rt/L})$, transpose the formula to make t the subject.

$$i = \frac{E}{R}(1 - e^{-Rt/L})$$

$$\frac{iR}{E} = 1 - e^{-Rt/L}$$

$$\therefore \; e^{-Rt/L} = 1 - \frac{iR}{E}$$

Taking logarithms to base 'e' of both sides,

$$-\frac{Rt}{L}\log e = \log\left(1 - \frac{iR}{E}\right)$$

$$\therefore \; -\frac{Rt}{L} = \log\left(\frac{E - iR}{E}\right)$$

$$\therefore \; -t = \frac{L}{R}\log\left(\frac{E - iR}{E}\right)$$

$$\therefore \; t = \frac{L}{R}\log\left(\frac{E}{E - iR}\right)$$

Example 2.13. Given $t = CR\log\left(\dfrac{V}{V - v}\right)$, find a formula for V.

$$t = CR\log\left(\frac{V}{V - v}\right)$$

$$\therefore \; \frac{t}{CR} = \log\left(\frac{V}{V - v}\right)$$

Using the definition of a logarithm,

$$e^{t/CR} = \frac{V}{V - v}$$

$$\therefore (V - v) e^{t/CR} = V$$

$$\therefore V e^{t/CR} - v e^{t/CR} = V$$

$$\therefore V e^{t/CR} - V = v e^{t/CR}$$

$$\therefore V(e^{t/CR} - 1) = v e^{t/CR}$$

$$\therefore V = \frac{v e^{t/CR}}{e^{t/CR} - 1}$$

Example 2.14. Given $G = \dfrac{V}{r \log (R/r)}$, transpose to make R the subject.

$$G = \frac{V}{r \log (R/r)}$$

$$\therefore Gr \log \left(\frac{R}{r}\right) = V$$

$$\therefore \log \left(\frac{R}{r}\right) = \frac{V}{Gr}$$

$$\therefore \frac{R}{r} = e^{V/Gr}$$

$$\therefore R = r e^{V/Gr}$$

It should be noted that in addition to the usual processes for transformation, explained in Volume 1 and Volume 2, the change from exponential to logarithmic form or vice versa is made only when the exponential or logarithmic term has been isolated, i.e., clear of **multiplying** coefficients and the addition or subtraction of other terms.

EXERCISE 2.3

Transpose the following formulae to make the indicated term the subject:

1. $T_1 = T_2 e^{\mu\theta}$ (μ)
2. $I = AT^2 e^{-b/T}$ (b)

3. $C = \dfrac{k}{\log\left[(d - r)/r\right]}$ (d)

4. $L = k \log\left(\dfrac{d_2}{d_1}\right)$ (d_2)

5. $q = A\,e^{-kt}$ (t)

6. $i = \dfrac{E}{R}\,e^{-t/CR}$ (C)

7. $\theta = \theta_f(1 - e^{-t/T})$ (T)

8. $G = \log\left(\dfrac{V_2}{V_1}\right)$ (V_1)

9. $v = V(1 - e^{-t/CR})$ (t)

10. $R = \dfrac{0\cdot 4343t}{C \log(d_1/d_2)}$ (d_1)

11. $C = \dfrac{kl}{2 \log(b/a)}$ (a)

12. $P_1 = P_2(V_2/V_1)^n$ (n)

13. $h = \dfrac{kv^n l}{2gd}$ (v)

14. (a) Show that the ratio $\log_a N/\log_b N$ is a constant for any number N, and calculate this constant if $a = 2$, $b = 3$.

(b) The formula $M = k \log\left[(d^2 + 4h^2)/d^2\right]$ describes the mutual inductance M of an open-wire pair at a height h above the ground. Change the subject of this formula to give h in terms of M, k, and d.

· C.G.L.I. T.T.

15. A transient current i amp at an instant t is given by,

$$i = \frac{E}{R}(1 - e^{-Rt/L})$$

If the ratio L/R is large compared with t, show that to a first approximation, i is directly proportional to t. Give a second approximation to i (neglecting t^3 and higher powers). Write a formula for L in terms of i, E, R, and t.

C.G.L.I. T.T. (part Qn.)

16. A body is projected vertically upwards with velocity u. If the air resistance is assumed to be $k \times$ (velocity)^2 per unit mass, then the height h attained is obtained from the formula,

$$u^2 = \frac{g}{k}(e^{2kh} - 1)$$

where g is constant. Make h the subject of this formula, and show that if k is small, then to the first approximation $u^2 = 2gh$. Derive a further approximation to u^2, not involving squares and higher powers of k.

C.G.L.I. T.T. (part Qn.)

17. If θ_0 and θ_h are the barometric readings at sea level and at a height h metres above sea level respectively, then, $h = a \log(\theta_0/\theta_h)$. Express θ_h in terms of h, a, and θ_0. A barometer reads 76·2 cm at sea level and 71·1 cm at 500 m. Find what it should read at 914·4 m.

C.G.L.I. T.T.

3. Calculus

3.1 Rate of change

In chapters 1 and 2 we have discussed at some length the idea of growth or general change in the values of variable quantities; by analysis of a systematic pattern, we can calculate values at some future stage. From $i = I_m e^{-t/RC}$, for example, we can calculate the value of an electric current i at a time t sec after some given starting time; or conversely, we can find the time when the value of the current will reach I amp. Mathematically, we are able to identify any position on a given graph.

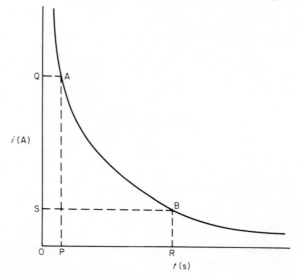

Fig. 3.1

In Fig. 3.1, given a value of t at P, we read the corresponding value of i at Q, and vice versa. We observe further, that at the time represented at R, the value of the current has changed to that represented at S; these two particular values may be a sufficient answer to some specific problem.

They raise the question, however, 'What is happening to the current between these two points?' We realize that the current has changed (past tense), but how fast is it changing (present tense)? The answer to this question would, so to speak, bring us up to date and provide us with more vital information than we have been able to obtain previously.

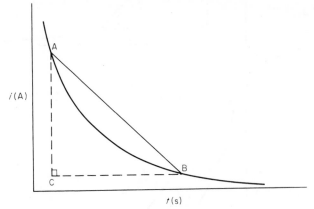

Fig. 3.2

In Fig. 3.2, the current has decreased between A and B by an amount represented by AC, during the time represented by CB. The rate of change of current per unit time is therefore represented by AC/CB amp/sec but this assumes that the change is uniform between A and B, i.e., the graph is the straight line AB. This assumption is obviously not true and AC/CB gives us only an average rate of change of current; the area between the chord AB and the curve is a measure of our error.

In Fig. 3.3, choosing the point A_1 nearer to B than A is, shows the chord A_1B nearer to the actual curve and we deduce that AC_1/C_1B is a more accurate measure of the rate of change of current. The improvement in accuracy is a result of diminishing the interval of time, C_1B; the answer, A_1C_1/C_1B, will still represent only an average rate of change as long as we continue to use the chords, AB, A_1B, etc. The accuracy will continue to improve as we make the intervals of measurement of t progressively smaller. For an ideal, absolute answer, the interval of measurement of t should be zero and hence the change in i would also be zero. The simple arithmetical method of calculating the

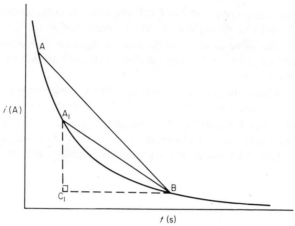

Fig. 3.3

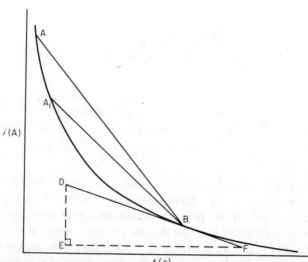

Fig. 3.4

rate of change, namely, AC/CB, would then give 0/0, which has no rational meaning.

Graphically, the chord has become a tangent to the curve at B, and geometrically the tangent is momentarily the same thing as the curve at the point of contact. By constructing a right-angled triangle, such as DEF, we could obtain the rate of change represented by the tangent by finding the ratio DE/EF; our answer, though valid, cannot be very accurate, having been obtained by drawing.

The methods of Calculus provide us with the means of calculating the required rate of change. We must first define what is expected of this new process.

Primarily, it must deal with extremely small quantities—practically equal to zero, and for the purpose of our illustration, it must show the meaning of the ratio of two of these quantities when one is dependent on the other; in other words, what is the meaning of

$$\frac{\text{an infinitely small measurement of current}}{\text{an infinitely small measurement of time}}?$$

Of course, all our problems are not connected with current, and we therefore use the more general variables, x and y. Generalizing in a similar fashion, we now ask the question, 'If y depends on x, at what rate is y changing as x changes?'

We shall show that one of the valuable aspects of calculus is its ability to give an instantaneous measurement of a changing situation in much the same way that a camera with a fast shutter, say $\frac{1}{500}$ sec, is able to produce a reasonably good photograph of a moving object; students should note that $\frac{1}{500}$ sec is in the 'very small' category, comparing in meaning, though not of course in size, with the 'infinitely small measurement of time' referred to previously.

The symbols δx and δy, pronounced 'delta x' and 'delta y', are used to denote small changes in the variables x and y, and replace the original measurements CB and AC in Fig. 3.2. The new ratio to be found therefore, is $\delta y/\delta x$ at the instant when δx becomes very small; we use the phrase 'let δx approach zero', and write $\delta x \to 0$ to show this. As δx approaches zero, so will δy, but it can be shown that the ratio $\delta y/\delta x$ will approach a 'finite limiting value', to which is given the symbol dy/dx. The idea of a finite limiting value has already been discussed in connection with certain geometrical progressions. In the series,

$$1, \tfrac{1}{2}, \tfrac{1}{4}, \tfrac{1}{8}, \ldots$$

the terms are continuing to become smaller and smaller, and though the sum of such terms will undoubtedly increase, it has been shown that the sum of an infinite number of terms has an upper limit of 2. The table below shows the sum of the first 20 terms at several stages.

Series	Sum
1, 0·5	1·5
1, 0·5, 0·25	1·75
1, 0·5, 0·25, 0·125	1·875
1, 0·5, 0·25, 0·125, 0·0625	1·9375
1, 0·5, 0·25, 0·125, 0·0625, 0·03125	1·96875
and if we take 10 terms,	1·99805
and if we take 20 terms,	1·999999

3.2   Differentiation; the operation dy/dx

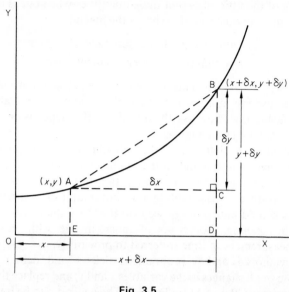

Fig. 3.5

Suppose $y = 3x^2 + 4x + 2$ represents a curve with co-ordinates x and y. Every point on the curve has two co-ordinate measurements x and y which must satisfy the given function.

We consider any point A on the curve, having co-ordinates (x, y) and a nearby point B having co-ordinates $(x + \delta x, y + \delta y)$; remember that δx means a small change in x. These latter co-ordinates must also agree with the given function since point B is also on the curve. Hence from $y = 3x^2 + 4x + 2$ we get

$$y + \delta y = 3(x + \delta x)^2 + 4(x + \delta x) + 2$$
$$= 3[x^2 + 2x\,\delta x + (\delta x)^2] + 4x + 4\,\delta x + 2$$
$$\therefore \ BD = y + \delta y = 3x^2 + 6x\,\delta x + 3(\delta x)^2 + 4x + 4\,\delta x + 2$$
$$AE = y \qquad = 3x^2 \qquad\qquad\qquad + 4x \qquad\quad + 2$$

$$\therefore \ BC = \quad \delta y = \quad\ + 6x\,\delta x + 3(\delta x)^2 \qquad + 4\,\delta x$$

dividing by δx,

$$\frac{\delta y}{\delta x} = 6x + 3\,\delta x + 4 \tag{3.1}$$

We now apply the following condition to the ratio $\delta y/\delta x$.

Let δx become infinitely small, i.e., let $\delta x \to 0$. Then δy will become infinitely small, i.e., $\delta y \to 0$ and $\delta y/\delta x$ will reach a limit, i.e., $\delta y/\delta x \to$ dy/dx. If $\delta x \to 0$, then relation (3.1) becomes,

$$\frac{dy}{dx} = 6x + 4$$

This method of obtaining dy/dx is known as 'by first principles'. The result is given the name 'differential coefficient' or 'derivative' of the function $3x^2 + 4x + 2$. We now have an accurate method of calculating the differential coefficient, although we used the graph as an illustration. If, however, we are going to use this new tool frequently then there must be a quicker means of finding it.

$$y = 3x^2 + 4x + 2$$

$$\therefore \quad \frac{dy}{dx} = 6x^1 + 4(x^0) \tag{3.2}$$

Compare
$$y = x^3 - x^2$$

$$\therefore \quad \frac{dy}{dx} = 3x^2 - 2x \tag{3.3}$$

Compare
$$y = \frac{1}{x^2}$$

$$\therefore \quad y = x^{-2}$$

$$\therefore \quad \frac{dy}{dx} = -2x^{-3} \tag{3.4}$$

Comparing the given functions with their differential coefficients, it can be seen at once that the powers of the independent variable x are the determining features of the differential coefficients; note that in (3.4) it is first essential to read the true power of x as -2, not as 2.

In general,

$$\text{if } y = x^n, \quad \text{then} \quad \frac{dy}{dx} = nx^{n-1}$$

or 'multiply by the power and take 1 from the power'. Note also that a constant in the given function produces no corresponding term in the differential coefficient. This is readily understandable if we think of a differential coefficient as a measure of change.

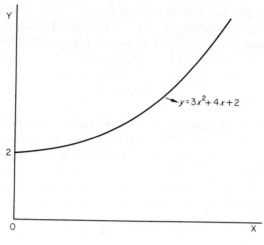

Fig. 3.6

The constant, 2, is purely a positional term and contributes nothing to the changing slope of the curve.

The following examples emphasize the need to express the true powers of the function clearly before applying the process of differentiation.

Example 3.1. $y = \sqrt{x^3}$

$$\therefore \quad y = x^{3/2}$$

$$\therefore \quad \frac{dy}{dx} = \frac{3x^{1/2}}{2}$$

Example 3.2. $y = (2x^2)^3$

$$\therefore \quad y = 8x^6$$

$$\therefore \quad \frac{dy}{dx} = 48x^5$$

Example 3.3. $y = (3x - 2)^2$

$$\therefore \quad y = 9x^2 - 12x + 4$$

$$\therefore \quad \frac{dy}{dx} = 18x - 12$$

Example 3.4. $y = 1/\sqrt{x}$

$$\therefore \quad y = x^{-1/2}$$

$$\therefore \quad \frac{dy}{dx} = -\frac{1}{2}x^{-3/2}$$

$$= -\frac{1}{2x^{3/2}}$$

In Example 3.4, it should be noted that a simplification has been made in the answer; for further calculation it is often useful to write all powers as positive.

3.3 Differentiation of a function of a function

The study and understanding of any branch of learning is greatly assisted by breaking down the subject into sections and giving each one a distinctive title; the meaning of this section may be clarified by considering the following illustration. An electric current in a circuit is a function of the e.m.f., which itself is a function of the chemical constituents of a battery or the physical construction of a generator, supplying the e.m.f. We now discuss this type of two-stage link mathematically.

Example 3.5. Find dy/dx if $y = (3x^2 + 5)^6$.

The given function is of the general form $y = x^n$, whose differentiation depends on the power n. The true power of the variable x in the given function is not at all clear but could be obtained by the application of the binomial expansion, producing seven terms; this is an unnecessarily prolonged calculation.

If $\qquad y = (3x^2 + 5)^6, \qquad$ let $\quad z = 3x^2 + 5$

$$\therefore \ y = z^6$$

$$\therefore \ \frac{dy}{dz} = 6z^5 \qquad\qquad \therefore \ \frac{dz}{dx} = 6x$$

The mathematical principles of a function of a function lead to a two-stage connection between y, z, and x.

Thus $\qquad\qquad \dfrac{dy}{dx} = \dfrac{dy}{dz} \times \dfrac{dz}{dx}$

$$\therefore \ \frac{dy}{dx} = 6z^5 \times 6x$$

$$\therefore \ \frac{dy}{dx} = 6(3x^2 + 5)^5 \times 6x$$

Example 3.6. Find ds/dt if $s = \sqrt{(t^2 - 3t + 5)}$.

If $s = \sqrt{(t^2 - 3t + 5)}$,   let $z = t^2 - 3t + 5$

$\therefore\ s = z^{1/2}$

$\therefore\ \dfrac{ds}{dz} = \dfrac{1}{2} z^{-1/2}$ $\therefore\ \dfrac{dz}{dt} = 2t - 3$

$\therefore\ \dfrac{ds}{dt} = \dfrac{ds}{dz} \times \dfrac{dz}{dt}$

$\therefore\ \dfrac{ds}{dt} = \dfrac{1}{2} z^{-1/2} \times (2t - 3)$

$\therefore\ \dfrac{ds}{dt} = \dfrac{1}{2\sqrt{(t^2 - 3t + 5)}} \times (2t - 3)$

3.4 Meaning and use of dy/dx

(a) The name, differential coefficient, implies a comparative measure of the rate at which two connected variables are changing; in the case of distance and time for example, it would represent velocity.

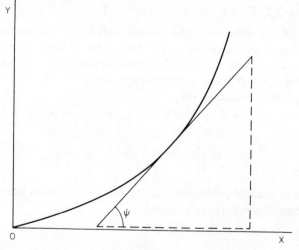

Fig. 3.7

(b) Graphically, dy/dx being associated with the tangent to the curve, it will also represent the slope or gradient of the curve at that particular point of contact.

(c) From Fig. 3.7 this also means that $dy/dx = \tan \psi$. It is very important to note that the angle ψ (pronounced 'psi') is always the angle
made by the tangent with the *positive* direction of x.

Example 3.7. A particle moves s m in time t sec given by the relation
$s = t^2 - 3t + 4$. Find its speed after 4 sec.

$$s = t^2 - 3t + 4 \qquad \text{(note 's' for displacement, not 'd')}$$

$$\text{Speed} = \text{rate of change of displacement per unit time}$$

$$= ds/dt$$

$$\therefore v = \frac{ds}{dt} = 2t - 3$$

At $t = 4$ sec,

$$v = 2 \times 4 - 3 = 5 \text{ m/s}$$

Example 3.8. Given $y = x^3/3 - 3x^2/2 - 4x + 1$, find (a) the gradient
on the corresponding graph, where $x = 2$ and (b) the values of x where
the gradient is zero.

(a)
$$y = \frac{x^3}{3} - \frac{3x^2}{2} - 4x + 1$$

$$\therefore \frac{dy}{dx} = \frac{3x^2}{3} - \frac{6x}{2} - 4$$

$$= x^2 - 3x - 4$$

At the point where $x = 2$, the gradient of the graph is,

$$2^2 - 3 \times 2 - 4 = 4 - 6 - 4$$
$$= -6$$

(b) If the gradient $= 0$, then

$$x^2 - 3x - 4 = 0$$
$$\therefore (x - 4)(x + 1) = 0$$
$$\therefore x = 4 \quad \text{or} \quad -1$$

Thus there are two points on the curve where the gradient is zero.

Example 3.9. A tangent is drawn to the curve $y = 3x^2/2 - 5x + 7$ at the point where $x = 2$. Calculate the angle between this tangent and the x-axis.

$$y = \frac{3x^2}{2} - 5x + 7$$

$$\therefore \frac{dy}{dx} = 3x - 5$$

At $x = 2$,

$$\frac{dy}{dx} = 6 - 5 = 1$$

$$\therefore \tan \psi = 1$$

$$\therefore \psi = 45°$$

The tangent meets the x-axis at $45°$.

Further use of dy/dx; equation of a tangent to a curve

A tangent, being a straight line, will have the general equation $y = mx + c$ where m and c are constants representing the gradient and intercept respectively.

Example 3.10. Find the equation of the tangent to the curve, $y = x^3 - x^2$ at the point where $x = 2$.

$$y = x^3 - x^2$$

$$\therefore \frac{dy}{dx} = 3x^2 - 2x$$

Therefore, at $x = 2$,

$$\frac{dy}{dx} = 8$$

Gradient of curve and of tangent at $x = 2$ is 8, i.e., m for the straight line is 8.

Equation of tangent is $y = 8x + c$.
At $x = 2$ on the curve, $y = 2^3 - 2^2 = 4$
At $x = 2$ on the line, $y = 4$

$$\text{from } y = 8x + c$$

$$4 = 8 \times 2 + c$$

$$\therefore -12 = c$$

Therefore, the equation of the tangent is $y = 8x - 12$.

3.5 Differentiation of e^x and $\log x$

It has been shown in a previous chapter that e^x represents the infinite series

$$e^x = 1 + x + \frac{x^2}{2!} + \frac{x^3}{3!} + \frac{x^4}{4!} + \cdots$$

$$\therefore \frac{d(e^x)}{dx} = 0 + 1 + \frac{2x}{2!} + \frac{3x^2}{3!} + \frac{4x^3}{4!} + \cdots$$

$$= 1 + x + \frac{x^2}{2!} + \frac{x^3}{3!} + \cdots$$

$$\therefore \frac{d(e^x)}{dx} = e^x$$

Example 3.11. Find the differential coefficients of

(a) e^{ax}, (b) e^{2x+3}, (c) e^{-x}

(a) Let $y = e^{ax}$ and let $z = ax$

$$\therefore y = e^z$$

$$\therefore \frac{dy}{dz} = e^z \qquad \text{and} \qquad \frac{dz}{dx} = a$$

Using the function of a function theorem,

$$\frac{dy}{dx} = \frac{dy}{dz} \times \frac{dz}{dx}$$

$$= e^z \times a$$

$$= a\, e^{ax}$$

(b) Let $y = e^{2x+3}$ and let $z = 2x + 3$

$$\therefore y = e^z$$

$$\therefore \frac{dy}{dz} = e^z \qquad \text{and} \qquad \frac{dz}{dx} = 2$$

$$\therefore \frac{dy}{dx} = \frac{dy}{dz} \times \frac{dz}{dx}$$

$$= e^z \times 2$$

$$\therefore \frac{dy}{dx} = 2\, e^{2x+3}$$

(c) Let $\quad y = e^{-x} \qquad\qquad$ and let $\quad z = -x$

$$\therefore \; y = e^z$$

$$\therefore \; \frac{dy}{dz} = e^z \qquad\qquad \text{and} \qquad \frac{dz}{dx} = -1$$

$$\therefore \; \frac{dy}{dx} = \frac{dy}{dz} \times \frac{dz}{dx}$$

$$= e^z \times (-1)$$

$$= -e^{-x}$$

Differentiation of log x

$$\text{Let } y = \log x$$

$$\therefore \; x = e^y$$

$$\therefore \; \frac{dx}{dy} = e^y$$

$$\therefore \; \frac{dy}{dx} = \frac{1}{e^y} = \frac{1}{x}$$

$$\therefore \; \frac{d(\log x)}{dx} = \frac{1}{x}$$

Example 3.12. Find the differential coefficients of (a) $\log 3x$, (b) $\log (2x + 3)$, (c) $\log (x^2 + 5x)$

(a) Let $\quad y = \log 3x \qquad\qquad$ and let $\quad z = 3x$

$$\therefore \; y = \log z$$

$$\therefore \; \frac{dy}{dz} = \frac{1}{z} \qquad\qquad \text{and} \qquad \frac{dz}{dx} = 3$$

$$\therefore \; \frac{dy}{dx} = \frac{dy}{dz} \times \frac{dz}{dx}$$

$$= \frac{1}{z} \times 3$$

$$= \frac{3}{3x} = \frac{1}{x}$$

It is interesting to note that this result is the same as the differential coefficient of $\log x$; the reason for this is simple to illustrate.

$$y = \log 3x = \log (3 \times x) = \log 3 + \log x$$

If $y = \log 3 + \log x$, then

$$\frac{dy}{dx} = 0 + \frac{1}{x} \quad \text{since } \log 3 \text{ is a constant.}$$

(b) Let $\quad y = \log(2x + 3)$ $\qquad$ and let $\quad z = 2x + 3$

$\qquad \therefore \; y = \log z$

$$\therefore \; \frac{dy}{dz} = \frac{1}{z} \qquad\qquad \text{and} \qquad \frac{dz}{dx} = 2$$

$$\therefore \; \frac{dy}{dx} = \frac{dy}{dz} \times \frac{dz}{dx}$$

$$= \frac{1}{z} \times 2 = \frac{2}{2x + 3}$$

(c) Let $\quad y = \log(x^2 + 5x)$ $\qquad$ and let $\quad z = x^2 + 5x$

$\qquad \therefore \; y = \log z$

$$\therefore \; \frac{dy}{dz} = \frac{1}{z} \qquad\qquad \text{and} \qquad \frac{dz}{dx} = 2x + 5$$

$$\therefore \; \frac{dy}{dx} = \frac{dy}{dz} \times \frac{dz}{dx}$$

$$= \frac{1}{z} \times (2x + 5)$$

$$= \frac{2x + 5}{x^2 + 5x}$$

Summary

If $y = e^{f(x)}$, then

$$\frac{dy}{dx} = f'(x)\, e^{f(x)}$$

If $y = \log f(x)$, then

$$\frac{dy}{dx} = \frac{f'(x)}{f(x)}$$

where $f'(x)$ represents the differential coefficient of $f(x)$.

3.6 Differentiation of products and quotients

(a) Product. A product is the result of multiplying two quantities. This must not be confused with applying two processes to one quantity.

6

$x^2 e^x$ is a product, but log (sin x) is a function of a function, there being only one quantity to which two processes have been applied.

If $y = u \times v$ where $u = f(x)$ and $v = F(x)$, then

$$\frac{dy}{dx} = u\frac{dv}{dx} + v\frac{du}{dx}$$

Without setting out a formal proof, the following geometrical illustration may promote the understanding of this theorem.

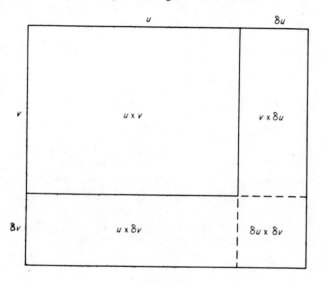

Fig. 3.8

If $y = u \times v$ and $u \times v$ represents the area of a rectangle, a small change in x causing corresponding changes δu and δv in u and v respectively will produce a change in area represented by δy. Therefore

$$\delta y = u\,\delta v + v\,\delta u + \delta u\,\delta v$$

The last term on the right is described as being of the 'second order of small quantities' and if δu and δv are infinitely small, this term can be neglected.

Hence

$$\delta y = u\,\delta v + v\,\delta u$$

from which

$$\frac{dy}{dx} = u\frac{dv}{dx} + v\frac{du}{dx}$$

Example 3.13. Find the differential coefficients of

$$\text{(a) } x^2 e^x, \quad \text{(b) } 2x^3 \log x, \quad \text{(c) } e^{2x} \log x$$

(a) Let $y = x^2 e^x$

$$\therefore \frac{dy}{dx} = x^2 e^x + e^x 2x$$

$$= x e^x (x + 2)$$

(b) Let $y = 2x^3 \log x$

$$\therefore \frac{dy}{dx} = 2x^3 \frac{1}{x} + \log x (6x^2)$$

$$= 2x^2 (1 + 3 \log x)$$

(c) Let $y = e^{2x} \log x$

$$\therefore \frac{dy}{dx} = e^{2x} \frac{1}{x} + (\log x)(2 e^{2x})$$

$$= e^{2x} \left(\frac{1}{x} + 2 \log x \right)$$

In words, the differential coefficient of a product is:

1st factor × d.c. of 2nd + 2nd factor × d.c. of 1st

(b) Quotient. A quotient is the result of dividing two quantities.
If $y = u/v$ where $u = f(x)$ and $v = F(x)$, then

$$\frac{dy}{dx} = \frac{v \dfrac{du}{dx} - u \dfrac{dv}{dx}}{v^2}$$

This formula does not lend itself to geometrical illustration, but is summarized in words as follows:

the d.c. of a quotient

$$= \frac{\text{denom.} \times \text{d.c. of numer.} - \text{numer.} \times \text{d.c. of denom.}}{(\text{denom.})^2}$$

Example 3.14. Find the d.c. of

$$\text{(a) } x^2/(3x - 1), \quad \text{(b) } e^{2x}/x^3, \quad \text{(c) } (\log x)/e^{3x}$$

(a) Let $y = x^2/(3x - 1)$

$$\therefore \frac{dy}{dx} = \frac{(3x - 1)2x - x^2 3}{(3x - 1)^2}$$

$$= \frac{6x^2 - 2x - 3x^2}{(3x - 1)^2}$$

$$= \frac{3x^2 - 2x}{(3x - 1)^2}$$

(b) Let $y = e^{2x}/x^3$

$$\therefore \frac{dy}{dx} = \frac{x^3 2 e^{2x} - e^{2x} 3x^2}{x^6}$$

$$= \frac{x^2 e^{2x}(2x - 3)}{x^6}$$

$$= \frac{e^{2x}(2x - 3)}{x^4}$$

(c) Let $y = (\log x)/e^{3x}$

$$\therefore \frac{dy}{dx} = \frac{e^{3x} \dfrac{1}{x} - \log x(3 e^{3x})}{e^{6x}}$$

$$= \frac{e^{3x}\left(\dfrac{1}{x} - 3 \log x\right)}{e^{6x}}$$

$$= \frac{\dfrac{1}{x} - 3 \log x}{e^{3x}}$$

EXERCISE 3.1

Differentiate the following functions, leaving the answers with positive powers.

1. $y = x^5$
2. $y = 4 - x^2$
3. $y = x - 2x^2$
4. $y = (3x + 1)^2$
5. $y = (x^4)^{1/3}$
6. $s = 2t^3 - t^2 + 3t + 1$

7. $p = \dfrac{2}{q^2}$

8. $p = \dfrac{1}{v}$

9. $h = \dfrac{10}{r^2}$

10. $V = \tfrac{4}{3}\pi R^3$

Find dy/dx for the following functions, other letters assumed constant.

11. $y = \dfrac{2x^4 + x^5}{x^3}$

12. $y = \sqrt{x}(2 - x)$

13. $y = \dfrac{1}{\sqrt[3]{x}}$

14. $y = \dfrac{3}{\sqrt{x}} - \dfrac{1}{x}$

15. $y = 3x^{-2}$

16. $y = ax^n$

17. $y = \dfrac{k}{x^a}$

18. $y = ax^2 + bx + c$

19. $y = \dfrac{a}{x} - bx$

20. $y = (x^a)^2 + x^b$

Find the gradients of the given curves at the given values of x.

21. $y = (2x + 5)(x - 2)$ at $x = 2$

22. $y = \dfrac{1}{\sqrt{x}}$ at $x = 9$

23. $y = (x^{1/2})^3$ at $x = 4$

24. $y = x^2 - 4x + 3$ at $x = 2$

25. $y = \dfrac{3x^2 - x^3}{x}$ at $x = 0$

Find dy/dx in the functions 26–40.

26. $y = (x^2 + 3x)^5$

27. $y = \sqrt{(1 + 4x)}$

28. $y = (1 - 2x + x^2)^{-3}$

29. $y = (x^3 - 2x^2)^{-1/2}$

30. $y = x^2 e^{3x}$

31. $y = (3x - 1) \log x$

32. $y = e^x \log x$

33. $y = (x + 2) e^{2x + 1}$

34. $y = e^{-0.5x}\sqrt{x}$

35. $y = \dfrac{x^2}{e^{3x}}$

36. $y = \dfrac{\log (2x + 1)}{3x}$

37. $y = \dfrac{3x + 5}{x^2}$

38. $y = \dfrac{1 + x}{1 - x}$ 39. $y = \log\left(\dfrac{1}{x}\right)$

40. $y = 3\,e^{2x} + 2\,e^{3x} + e$.

41. The relation between the anode current I and the grid voltage V of a certain triode valve may be taken as,

$$I = 6 + 3V + \tfrac{1}{2}V^2$$

Find, by differentiation, the rate of change of anode current when the grid voltage is 2. Find also the value of V which makes $dI/dV = 1$.

E.M.E.U. (part Qn.)

42. A coil has a self inductance of 4 H and a resistance of 200 Ω. A d.c. supply of 100 V is applied to the coil. The instantaneous current i A is given by,

$$i = \dfrac{E}{R}\left(1 - e^{-Rt/L}\right)$$

Find (a) the rate at which the current increases at the moment of switching on, and (b) the rate after 0·01 sec.

43. A fully charged capacitor of 0·2 μF has a p.d. of 150 V between the plates; it is then discharged through a resistor of 1·5 MΩ. If the p.d. across the plates at any time t sec after closing the circuit is given by

$$v = V\,e^{-t/RC}$$

Calculate, (a) the initial rate of loss of voltage, and (b) the rate after 0·1 sec.

3.7 Graphical derivation of the differentiation of sin θ

If $y = \sin\theta$ we require to find $dy/d\theta$, which represents the gradient of the graph. Figure 3.9 shows the graph of $\sin\theta$, identified at points A, B, C, etc. The values of the gradients at these points are plotted on a second set of axes in a corresponding position below.

At A, the gradient is positive and steepest, giving A′ a maximum positive value on $dy/d\theta$.

At B, the gradient is still positive but diminishing, giving point B′.

At C, the gradient is zero, giving point C′.

At D, the gradient is now negative and increasing in numerical value, giving point D′.

At E, the gradient is steepest and remains negative, giving point E′ a minimum value.

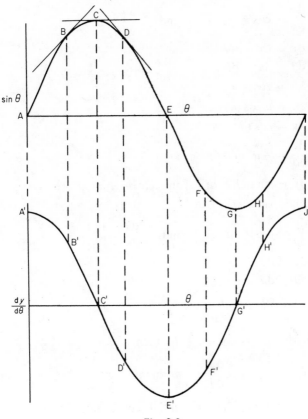

Fig. 3.9

It is a useful exercise for the student to complete a similar series of statements for the remaining points. The complete graph for $dy/d\theta$ is now recognized as being the graph of $\cos\theta$. Hence,

$$\text{if } y = \sin\theta, \quad \text{then} \quad dy/d\theta = \cos\theta \qquad (3.5)$$

Similarly it can be shown that,

$$\text{if } y = \cos\theta, \quad \text{then} \quad dy/d\theta = -\sin\theta \qquad (3.6)$$

3.8 Differentiation of $\sin(a\theta)$, $\cos(a\theta)$, $\sin(a\theta + b)$, $\cos(a\theta + b)$

(a) Let $y = \sin(a\theta)$ and let $u = a\theta$

$\therefore y = \sin u$

$$\therefore \quad \frac{dy}{du} = \cos u \qquad \text{and} \qquad \frac{du}{d\theta} = a$$

$$\therefore \quad \frac{dy}{d\theta} = \frac{dy}{du} \times \frac{du}{d\theta}$$

$$= \cos u \times a$$

$$= a \cos (a\theta) \qquad (3.7)$$

(b) Let $y = \cos (a\theta)$

$$\therefore \quad \frac{dy}{d\theta} = -a \sin (a\theta) \qquad (3.8)$$

(c) Let $y = \sin (a\theta + b)$ and let $u = a\theta + b$

$$\therefore \quad y = \sin u$$

$$\therefore \quad \frac{dy}{du} = \cos u \qquad \text{and} \qquad \frac{du}{d\theta} = a$$

$$\therefore \quad \frac{dy}{d\theta} = \frac{dy}{du} \times \frac{du}{d\theta}$$

$$= \cos u \times a$$

$$= a \cos (a\theta + b) \qquad (3.9)$$

(d) Similarly, if $y = \cos (a\theta + b)$, then

$$\frac{dy}{d\theta} = -a \sin (a\theta + b) \qquad (3.10)$$

Example 3.15. Find the differential coefficients of the following functions.

    (a) $e^x \sin x$ (b) $t^3 \sin 2t$

    (c) $e^{2t} \sin (3t + \pi)$ (d) $e^{-t} \sin \left(2\pi ft + \dfrac{\pi}{3}\right)$

    (e) $2 \sin \omega t \cos \omega t$ (f) $\tan \theta$

(a) Let $y = e^x \sin x$

$$\therefore \quad \frac{dy}{dx} = e^x \cos x + \sin x \, e^x$$

$$= e^x(\cos x + \sin x)$$

(b) Let $y = t^3 \sin 2t$

$$\therefore \quad \frac{dy}{dt} = t^3 2 \cos 2t + \sin 2t \, 3t^2$$

$$= t^2(2t \cos 2t + 3 \sin 2t)$$

(c) Let $y = e^{2t} \sin (3t + \pi)$

$$\therefore \frac{dy}{dt} = e^{2t} 3 \cos (3t + \pi) + \sin (3t + \pi).2 e^{2t}$$

$$= e^{2t} [3 \cos (3t + \pi) + 2 \sin (3t + \pi)]$$

(d) Let $y = e^{-t} \sin (2\pi ft + \pi/3)$

$$\therefore \frac{dy}{dt} = e^{-t} 2\pi f \cos \left(2\pi ft + \frac{\pi}{3} \right) + \sin \left(2\pi ft + \frac{\pi}{3} \right).(-e^{-t})$$

$$= e^{-t} \left[2\pi f \cos \left(2\pi ft + \frac{\pi}{3} \right) - \sin \left(2\pi ft + \frac{\pi}{3} \right) \right]$$

(e) Let $y = 2 \sin \omega t \cos \omega t$

$$\therefore \frac{dy}{dt} = 2 \sin \omega t(-\omega \sin \omega t) + \cos \omega t(2\omega \cos \omega t)$$

$$= 2\omega(\cos^2 \omega t - \sin^2 \omega t)$$

(f) Let $y = \tan \theta = \sin \theta/\cos \theta$

$$\therefore \frac{dy}{d\theta} = \frac{\cos \theta \cos \theta - \sin \theta(-\sin \theta)}{\cos^2}$$

$$= \frac{\cos^2 \theta + \sin^2 \theta}{\cos^2 \theta}$$

$$= \frac{1}{\cos^2 \theta}$$

$$= \sec^2 \theta$$

EXERCISE 3.2

1. Differentiate the following functions.
   (a) $\sin 100t$
   (b) $3 \cos \omega t$
   (c) $2 \sin (50t - \pi)$
   (d) $\frac{1}{2} \cos (2\pi ft + \pi/2)$
   (e) $I_m \sin (20t - 0.2)$
   (f) $V_m \cos \theta + IR \sin 2\theta$

2. Find the differential coefficient of the following products.
   (a) $e^{2t} \sin t$
   (b) $\sin 2\theta \cos 3\theta$
   (c) $(\cos t) \times e^{-t}$
   (d) $e^{2\theta} \sin (3\theta - \pi/3)$
   (e) $\log 3x \cos x$
   (f) $e^{\omega t} \sin 2\omega t$

3. Find the derivative of the following quotients.

(a) $\dfrac{\sin \theta}{1 - \cos \theta}$

(b) $\dfrac{e^x}{\sin x}$

(c) $\cot \theta$

(d) $\dfrac{\cos 2t}{e^{-2t}}$

(e) $\cot \omega t$

(f) $\dfrac{2t}{\cos (10t - 0\cdot2)}$

4. Find the gradient on the graph of $y = \sin \theta$ when $\theta = \pi/3$.

5. An alternating current is given by $i = 50 \sin 2\pi ft$. Find the rate of change of current after 0·01 sec, given that $f = 50$ Hz.

6. An alternating voltage is given by $v = 100 \sin (20t + \pi/3)$ V. Calculate the rate at which the voltage is changing after 0·02 sec.

7. Find the smallest positive value of θ for which the gradient of the graph of $2 \sin \theta + 4 \cos \theta$ is zero.

8. A quantity which varies sinusoidally is given by

$$P = 10 \sin (\omega t + 0\cdot1)$$

Find the time t sec when the gradient is first zero, given that $\omega = 100\pi$ rad/sec.

9. If $i = 10 \sin 2\omega t$ and $v = 20 \cos 2\omega t$, calculate the first positive value of t for which i and v have the same rate of change, given that $\omega = 50$ rad/sec.

10. Calculate the first range of values of θ for which the graph of $y = \sin \theta + \cos \theta$ has a negative gradient.

11. Calculate the co-ordinates of the point on the graph of $y = \cos 2\theta$ at which the gradient is first equal to 0·5.

4. Applications of the differential coefficient

4.1 Time, distance, velocity

If a displacement of s m takes place in a time t sec, we say that s is a function of t and write $s = f(t)$, $F(t)$, or $\phi(t)$. By differentiating this function and obtaining ds/dt, we are able to calculate the numerical value of velocity, since ds/dt measures the rate of change of displacement per unit time. Applying the process of differentiation once more, we should be expressing a rate of change of velocity, i.e., an acceleration.

Hence, if $s = f(t)$

$$v = \frac{ds}{dt} = f'(t)$$

and

$$a = \frac{dv}{dt} = f''(t)$$

where $f'(t)$ and $f''(t)$ represent the first and second differentials of $f(t)$ respectively. The expression for acceleration could therefore be written as,

$$\frac{d\left(\dfrac{ds}{dt}\right)}{dt} \quad \text{abbreviated to} \quad \frac{d^2s}{dt^2}$$

Example 4.1. A body moves a distance of s m in time t sec according to $s = t^3 - 3t^2$. Calculate its velocity after 3 sec and after 2 sec.

$$s = t^3 - 3t^2$$

$$\therefore \; v = \frac{ds}{dt} = 3t^2 - 6t$$

At $t = 3$, $v = 3 \times 3^2 - 6 \times 3 = 9$ m/sec

At $t = 2$, $v = 3 \times 2^2 - 6 \times 2 = 0$ m/sec

Of these two velocities, the zero value is the more significant and in fact we can give a physical meaning to each of the critical values, $s = 0$, $v = 0$, and $t = 0$.

$s = 0$; the body is at the starting point or has returned to it.

$v = 0$; the body has stopped, possibly only momentarily.

$t = 0$; when this condition is applied in the velocity function, we are measuring the initial velocity, i.e., the velocity at the beginning of our period of observation or measurement.

Example 4.2. If a body moves s m in t sec, and

$$s = \frac{2t^3}{3} - \frac{5t^2}{2} + 3t$$

find the times when the body will be stationary and the distances from the starting point at these times.

$$s = \frac{2t^3}{3} - \frac{5t^2}{2} + 3t$$

$$\therefore \; v = \frac{ds}{dt} = 2t^2 - 5t + 3$$

When $v = 0$, $2t^2 - 5t + 3 = 0$

$$\therefore \; (2t - 3)(t - 1) = 0$$

$$\therefore \; t = 1\tfrac{1}{2} \text{ or } 1 \text{ sec}$$

The body is at rest after 1 sec and again after $1\tfrac{1}{2}$ sec.

At $t = 1$, $s = \tfrac{2}{3} - \tfrac{5}{2} + 3 = 1\tfrac{1}{6}$ m

At $t = \tfrac{3}{2}$, $s = \tfrac{2}{3}(\tfrac{3}{2})^3 - \tfrac{5}{2}(\tfrac{3}{2})^2 + \tfrac{9}{2}$

$$= \tfrac{9}{4} - \tfrac{45}{8} + \tfrac{9}{2}$$

$$= 1\tfrac{1}{8} \text{ m}$$

Example 4.3. A particle moves s m in t sec, and

$$s = t^3 - 6t^2 + 8t$$

Calculate the velocity each time it passes the starting point.

When $s = 0$,

$$t^3 - 6t^2 + 8t = 0$$
$$\therefore \ t(t^2 - 6t + 8) = 0$$
$$\therefore \ t(t - 2)(t - 4) = 0$$
$$\therefore \ t = 0, 2, \text{ or } 4 \text{ sec}$$

The particle passes the starting point after 2 sec and again after 4 sec.

$$s = t^3 - 6t^2 + 8t$$

$$\therefore \ v = \frac{\mathrm{d}s}{\mathrm{d}t} = 3t^2 - 12t + 8$$

At $t = 2$,

$$v = 3 \times 2^2 - 12 \times 2 + 8$$
$$= -4 \text{ m/sec}$$

The negative value indicates motion in the opposite direction to the original one, i.e., the particle is returning to the starting point for the first time.

At $t = 4$,

$$v = 3 \times 4^2 - 12 \times 4 + 8$$
$$= 8 \text{ m/sec}$$

The positive value indicates that the direction of motion has changed once more and is now in the original direction.

4.2   Inductance and capacitance

The p.d. induced in an inductor is proportional to the rate of change of current through the inductor, and is such as to oppose the direction of the current. This can be expressed symbolically in mathematical terms, using a differential coefficient.

$$\text{Rate of change of current} = \frac{\mathrm{d}i}{\mathrm{d}t}$$

$$\text{p.d. produced, } e \propto \frac{\mathrm{d}i}{\mathrm{d}t}$$

$$\therefore \ e = -k \frac{\mathrm{d}i}{\mathrm{d}t}$$

The constant of proportionality, k, is the measure of that property of the inductor to which is given the term self inductance and represented by L. Hence

$$e = -L \frac{di}{dt}$$

Example 4.4. If a current i mA is given in terms of t by $i = t^2 - 4t$, and produces a p.d. of 8 mV in an inductor after 3 sec, calculate the constant of proportionality and hence find the p.d. after 4 sec.

$$i = t^2 - 4t$$

$$\therefore \frac{di}{dt} = 2t - 4$$

At $t = 3$,
$$\frac{di}{dt} = 2 \times 3 - 4 = 2$$

$$\therefore \text{ from } e = -k \frac{di}{dt}$$

$$8 = k \times 2 \quad \text{(numerically)}$$

$$\therefore k = 4$$

$$\therefore e = 4 \times \frac{di}{dt} \quad \text{(numerically)}$$

At $t = 4$,
$$\frac{di}{dt} = 4$$

$$\therefore e = 4 \times 4 = 16 \text{ mV}$$

Capacitance

A similar property can be deduced for a capacitor when being charged or discharged. An electric current can be considered as a continuous transfer of charge; the value of the current is proportional to the rate of transfer of charge. Hence

$$i \propto \frac{dq}{dt}$$

$$\therefore i = k \frac{dq}{dt}$$

The units of charge and current are so chosen as to make $k = 1$. Therefore

$$i = \frac{dq}{dt}$$

or

$$i\,dt = dq$$

The increase in p.d. across a capacitor is proportional to this charge.

$$dv \propto dq$$

or

$$dq = c\,dv$$

$$\therefore\ i\,dt = c\,dv$$

$$\therefore\ i = c\frac{dv}{dt}$$

The constant of proportionality, c, is therefore a measure of the property of the capacitor to which is given the term capacitance and represented by C. Hence

$$i = C\frac{dv}{dt}$$

Example 4.5. A voltage v V given in terms of t by $v = 4t^2$ is applied to a capacitor and produces a current of 0·8 mA after 1 sec. Calculate the capacitance and hence the current after 2 sec.

$$v = 4t^2$$

$$\therefore\ \frac{dv}{dt} = 8t$$

At $t = 1$,

$$\frac{dv}{dt} = 8$$

and from

$$i = C\frac{dv}{dt}$$

$$\therefore\ 10^{-3} \times 0{\cdot}8 = C \times 8$$

$$\therefore\ C = 10^{-4} = 100\ \mu F$$

$$\therefore\ i = 10^{-4} \times 8t$$

After 2 sec,

$$i = 10^{-4} \times 16$$

$$\therefore\ i = 1{\cdot}6\ mA$$

4.3 Alternating current

It has been shown in Volume 2 that a radius vector rotating at a constant angular velocity will produce a sinusoidal wave-form representing an alternating current $i = I_m \sin \omega t$ or an alternating voltage $v = V_m \sin \omega t$.

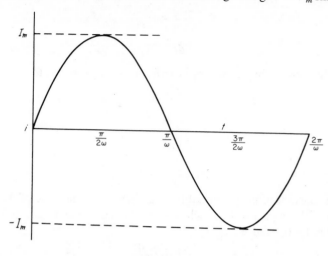

Fig. 4.1

The application of differentiation to the functions, i and v, has an important bearing on the calculation of current and voltage variation in an a.c. circuit containing inductance and capacitance.

Alternating current in a circuit possessing only inductance

It is important that the terms describing the quantities involved are clearly understood. There are two voltages to be considered: the applied voltage of the alternating supply, which we shall call v volts, and the induced voltage in the inductor, which we shall call e volts, and the alternating current, i amperes.

The instantaneous value e of the voltage induced in the inductor is given by Lenz's law,

$$e = -L \frac{di}{dt}$$

We suppose the alternating current to be given by,

$$i = I_m \sin \omega t \tag{4.1}$$

$$\therefore \frac{di}{dt} = \omega I_m \cos \omega t$$

$$\therefore e = -L\omega I_m \cos \omega t \tag{4.2}$$

(4.1) and (4.2) are represented graphically in Fig. 4.2, the vertical axis having separate scales, graduated for i and v.

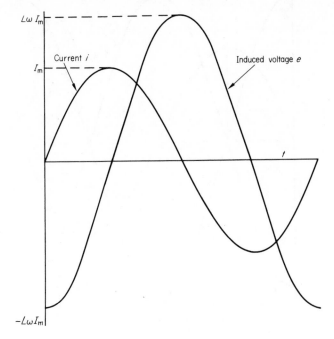

Fig. 4.2

We have assumed that the circuit has negligible resistance and hence the applied voltage is absorbed entirely by the induced voltage e. Therefore

$$v = L\omega I_m \cos \omega t \qquad (4.3)$$

note the opposite sign in (4.2).

Equations (4.1), (4.2) and (4.3) are represented graphically in Fig. 4.3. There are three important conclusions to be drawn from Fig. 4.3:

(a) the applied voltage leads the current by $\frac{1}{4}$-cycle;
(b) the graphs of e and v are mirror images of each other in the horizontal axis; the algebraic sum of their ordinates is zero;
(c) i, e, and v are alternating quantities which vary sinusoidally.

In direct current theory, the ratio voltage/current, by Ohm's law, describes the property of the circuit which we call resistance. A similar comparison is now made using alternating quantities.

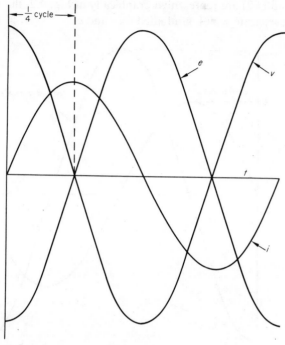

Fig. 4.3

From (4.1), the maximum value of current, $= I_m$

From (4.3), the maximum value of voltage, $V_m = L\omega I_m$

Hence $V_m/I_m = \omega L$, and similarly, using r.m.s. values,

$$\frac{V}{I} = \frac{V_m}{\sqrt{2}} \div \frac{I_m}{\sqrt{2}} = \omega L = 2\pi f L, \quad \text{since } \omega = 2\pi f$$

The property of the circuit, measured by $2\pi f L$, is called the inductive reactance, expressed in ohms and represented by X_L. Hence

$$\frac{V}{I} = 2\pi f L = X_L \qquad (4.4)$$

or
$$I = \frac{V}{X_L} = \frac{V}{2\pi f L} \qquad (4.5)$$

From (4.4), $X_L = 2\pi f L$, it can be seen that the inductive reactance is directly proportional to the frequency, giving a straight-line graph.

From (4.5), $I = V/2\pi f L$, the current is inversely proportional to the frequency, as shown graphically in Fig. 4.4.

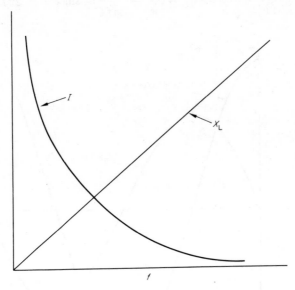

Fig. 4.4

Alternating current possessing only capacitance

In section 4.2, it was shown that $i = C(dv/dt)$, i.e., the current in a capacitive circuit depends on the rate of change of applied voltage. Consequently, we first assume an a.c. supply given by,

$$v = V_m \sin \omega t \quad \text{(or } v = V_m \sin 2\pi ft) \tag{4.6}$$

$$\therefore \frac{dv}{dt} = \omega V_m \cos \omega t$$

$$\therefore i = C\omega V_m \cos \omega t \tag{4.7}$$

Equations (4.6) and (4.7) are represented graphically in Fig. 4.5, the vertical axis having separate scales graduated for i and v.

There are two important conclusions to be drawn from Fig. 4.5.

(a) the current leads the applied voltage by $\frac{1}{4}$-cycle;

(b) i and v are alternating quantities which vary sinusoidally.

From (4.6), the maximum value of applied voltage $= V_m$

From (4.7), the maximum value of current $\quad = \omega C V_m$

Hence $V_m/I_m = 1/\omega C$, and similarly using r.m.s. values,

$$\frac{V}{I} = \frac{V_m}{\sqrt{2}} \div \frac{I_m}{\sqrt{2}} = \frac{1}{\omega C} = \frac{1}{2\pi f C}, \quad \text{since } \omega = 2\pi f$$

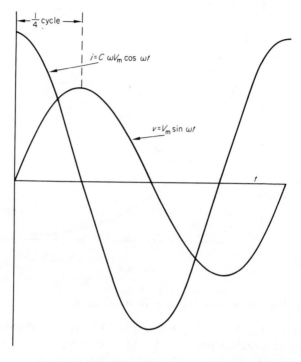

Fig. 4.5

The property of the circuit, measured by $1/(2\pi f C)$, is called the capacitive reactance, expressed in ohms and represented by X_C. Hence

$$\frac{V}{I} = \frac{1}{2\pi f C} = X_C \qquad (4.8)$$

or

$$\frac{V}{X_C} = I = 2\pi f C V \qquad (4.9)$$

From (4.8), $X_C = 1/(2\pi f C)$, it can be seen that capacitive reactance is inversely proportional to the frequency, shown graphically in Fig. 4.6.

From (4.9), $I = 2\pi f C V$, the current is directly proportional to the frequency, giving a straight-line graph.

The purpose of the examples in sections 4.1, 4.2, and 4.3 has been to show that it is often more useful to consider the rate at which quantities are changing, rather than a particular value which they have reached, and that the process of differentiation provides a simple measure of rate of change in dy/dx.

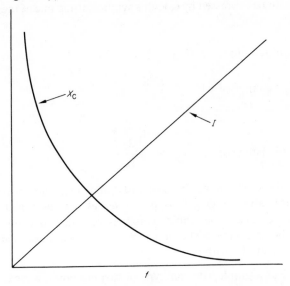

Fig. 4.6

4.4   Maximum and minimum turning points

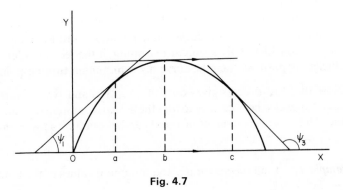

Fig. 4.7

Consider a curve as shown, with tangents drawn at points with values of $x = a$, b, and c.

Since ψ_1 is acute, then $\tan \psi_1$ is positive, and since ψ_3 is obtuse, then $\tan \psi_3$ is negative.

It is obvious that ψ_2 is zero, i.e., the angle made by the tangent at $x = b$ is zero since the tangent is parallel to the x-axis. As the value of x increases through a, b, and c, the gradient of the curve changes from positive, through zero to negative, i.e., the gradient is decreasing. This change can be expressed by calculus symbols using one of the meanings of dy/dx.

Equation of curve $\qquad y = f(x)$

Rate of change of y $\qquad = \dfrac{dy}{dx}$

Rate of change of gradient $= \dfrac{d\left(\dfrac{dy}{dx}\right)}{dx}$

Since the elements of this last operation, i.e., numerator and denominator, are changing in opposite senses, i.e., as x increases, the gradient decreases, the whole symbol is regarded as being negative. The symbol is abbreviated to d^2y/dx^2 and is called the second differential coefficient of y with respect to x.

Rule. For a graph with this type of turning-point, a maximum, the following conditions apply.
1. Find dy/dx and let $dy/dx = 0$ and solve this equation; suppose there are two solutions, $x = b_1$ and $x = b_2$.
2. Find d^2y/dx^2 and by substitution of the values $x = b_1$ and $x = b_2$ consider the sign of the function d^2y/dx^2 in each case separately. If the sign is negative, then the curve has a maximum turning-point at the value of x considered. By a similar reasoning, if the second differential coefficient is positive, then the curve has a minimum turning-point.

Note that this process gives only the position and type of turning-point; it may also be necessary to find the actual maximum or minimum value. This is a measurement of y and can be found by substitution of $x = b_1$ or $x = b_2$ in $y = f(x)$.

Example 4.6. Find the maximum and minimum values of the function $x^3 + 3x^2 - 9x$.

Let $y = x^3 + 3x^2 - 9x$

$$\therefore \frac{dy}{dx} = 3x^2 + 6x - 9$$

Condition 1. Let $dy/dx = 0$ and solve.

$$\therefore\ 3x^2 + 6x - 9 = 0$$
$$\therefore\ x^2 + 2x - 3 = 0$$
$$\therefore\ (x + 3)(x - 1) = 0$$
$$\therefore\ x = -3 \text{ or } x = 1 \qquad (4.10)$$

So far we have established that there are two turning-points whose positions are at $x = -3$ and $x = 1$; we must now determine the types of turning-points, for which the second d.c. is required.

$$\frac{dy}{dx} = 3x^2 + 6x - 9$$

$$\therefore\ \frac{d^2y}{dx^2} = 6x + 6$$

Substitute the position values of x found in (4.10) above:

At $x = -3$,
$$\frac{d^2y}{dx^2} = 6(-3) + 6$$
$$= -12$$

Under condition 2, this negative value indicates that the function has a maximum value at $x = -3$. In general at this stage in the study of calculus, the student must expect that the turning-point at the other value of x is of the opposite type. It will be shown later where necessary, that special cases arise where this is not true. We must establish that this second turning-point is a minimum.

At $x = 1$,
$$\frac{d^2y}{dx^2} = 6(1) + 6$$
$$= 12$$

The positive value of this last operator thus indicates that there is a minimum value of the original function at $x = 1$.

It can be seen from the graph that the size of the maximum and minimum values is a measurement of y; we refer to the original function.

$$y = x^3 + 3x^2 - 9x$$
At $x = -3$,
$$y = (-3)^3 + 3(-3)^2 - 9(-3)$$
$$= -27 + 27 + 27$$
$$= 27$$
At $x = 1$,
$$y = 1^3 + 3(1)^2 - 9(1)$$
$$= -5$$

Therefore the maximum value of $x^3 + 3x^2 - 9x$ is 27 and the minimum value of $x^3 + 3x^2 - 9x$ is -5.

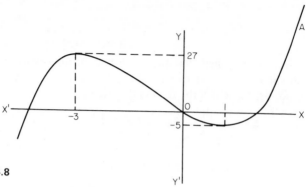

Fig. 4.8

A maximum turning-point on a graph is such that its value is greater than the values immediately preceding and following it. It does not mean that it is the largest value plotted on the graph. The section of graph at A will continue to rise above the value $y = 27$. The same general meaning is attached to a minimum turning-point.

The use of the second d.c. to distinguish between turning-points is describing the change in gradient. This method can be replaced by a purely numerical analysis of the gradient on each side of a turning-point.

In Example 4.6, $dy/dx = 3x^2 + 6x - 9$, giving turning-points at $x = -3$ or 1.

At $x = -4$, $\dfrac{dy}{dx} = 3(-4)^2 + 6(-4) - 9 = 15$

At $x = -2$, $\dfrac{dy}{dx} = 3(-2)^2 + 6(-2) - 9 = -9$

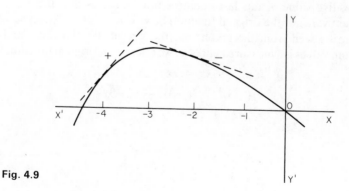

Fig. 4.9

The positive and negative gradients shown dotted in Fig. 4.9 indicate a maximum turning-point. The student should complete a similar application for the other turning-point at $x = 1$.

Example 4.7. Find the turning-point on $y = (4 - x)^2$ and state the type.

Let $y = (4 - x)^2$

$$\therefore \ y = 16 - 8x + x^2$$

$$\therefore \ \frac{dy}{dx} = -8 + 2x$$

$$\therefore \ \frac{d^2y}{dx^2} = +2$$

Condition 1. Let $dy/dx = 0$

$$\therefore \ -8 + 2x = 0$$

$$\therefore \ x = 4$$

There is only one turning-point on the graph, at $x = 4$, and on examination of d^2y/dx^2, we note that it already shows a positive sign independent of any value of x, indicating a minimum turning point.

Summary

Differentiation. If $y = x^n$, then $dy/dx = nx^{n-1}$.

Meaning of dy/dx. 1. A rate measurer
2. Gradient or slope of a curve
3. $dy/dx = \tan \psi$

Turning points. 1. Let $dy/dx = 0$ and solve
2. Test d^2y/dx^2 for sign
+ve means minimum, −ve means maximum

4.5 Problems on maxima and minima

The object of this type of problem is to calculate a 'best solution' between two extremes. To reach the top of a hill in the shortest time, we might consider the direct route, which would be shortest in distance, but because of its steepest gradient, might not be shortest in time. An alternative route, taking a much more gradual gradient, would be much longer in distance, thus increasing the time taken. There is always a 'best solution' somewhere between these extremes. It is important to identify the dimension for which a maximum or minimum value is required.

Example 4.8. A farmer has 100 m of loose fencing with which he proposes to enclose a rectangular plot of maximum area using a natural hedge as one boundary. Calculate the required dimensions of the plot.

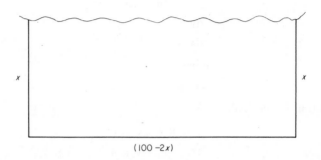

(100 −2x)

Fig. 4.10

Let the width of the plot be x m

$$\therefore \text{ Length} = (100 - 2x) \text{ m}$$
$$\therefore \text{ Area}, A = x(100 - 2x) \text{ m}^2$$
$$= 100x - 2x^2$$
$$\therefore \frac{\mathrm{d}A}{\mathrm{d}x} = 100 - 4x$$
$$\therefore \frac{\mathrm{d}^2A}{\mathrm{d}x^2} = -4$$

Let $\mathrm{d}A/\mathrm{d}x = 0$

$$\therefore 100 - 4x = 0$$
$$\therefore x = 25$$

Since $\mathrm{d}^2A/\mathrm{d}x^2$ is negative, the turning-point when $x = 25$ is a maximum. Hence the required dimensions are 25×50 m.

Example 4.9. The cost of running a certain generator is £P per hour at N rev/min where P is given by,

$$P = 3 \cdot 2 \times 10^{-7}N^2 - 1 \cdot 6 \times 10^{-3}N + 5$$

Calculate the most economical speed in rev/min.

$$P = 3\cdot2 \times 10^{-7}N^2 - 1\cdot6 \times 10^{-3}N + 5$$

$$\therefore \frac{\mathrm{d}P}{\mathrm{d}N} = 3\cdot2 \times 10^{-7} \times 2N - 1\cdot6 \times 10^{-3}$$

$$\therefore \frac{\mathrm{d}^2P}{\mathrm{d}N^2} = 3\cdot2 \times 10^{-7} \times 2$$

Let $\mathrm{d}P/\mathrm{d}N = 0$

$$\therefore 3\cdot2 \times 10^{-7} \times 2N - 1\cdot6 \times 10^{-3} = 0$$

$$\therefore N = \frac{1\cdot6 \times 10^{-3}}{3\cdot2 \times 10^{-7} \times 2}$$

$$\therefore N = 2500$$

Since $\mathrm{d}^2P/\mathrm{d}N^2$ is positive, then P is a minimum when the speed is 2500 rev/min.

Example 4.10.

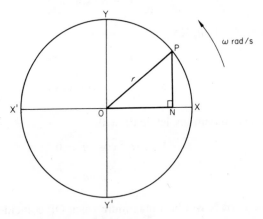

Fig. 4.11

In the given figure, a radius arm OP rotates at a constant angular velocity ω rad/sec. Find (a) an expression for the velocity of the point N along XX' at any time t sec, (b) the position of the arm OP for this velocity to be a maximum. Show that the acceleration of the point N is proportional to its distance from O.

(a) After t sec, the angle PON will be ωt rad. Let the length ON be x, and let the length OP be r.

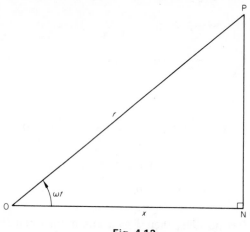

Fig. 4.12

$$\therefore \quad x = r \cos \omega t$$

$$\therefore \quad \frac{\mathrm{d}x}{\mathrm{d}t} = -r\omega \sin \omega t$$

Velocity of N along XX' $= -r\omega \sin \omega t$.

(b) $$v = -r\omega \sin \omega t$$

$$\therefore \quad a = \frac{\mathrm{d}v}{\mathrm{d}t} = -r\omega^2 \cos \omega t$$

For v to be a maximum, let $\mathrm{d}v/\mathrm{d}t = 0$

$$\therefore \quad -r\omega^2 \cos \omega t = 0$$

$$\therefore \quad \omega t = \frac{\pi}{2}$$

The velocity of N will be a maximum when OP coincides with OY.

$$a = -r\omega^2 \cos \omega t$$
$$= -\omega^2(r \cos \omega t)$$
$$= -\omega^2 x$$

Acceleration is directly proportional to the distance of N from O since ω is constant. The point N is said to move with simple harmonic motion (S.H.M.).

Example 4.11. Find the area of the ground plan of the greatest rect-angular building which can be erected on a plot of ground in the shape of an equilateral triangle whose side is 30 m assuming that one side of the building lies along one side of the triangle.

E.M.E.U. (part Qn.)

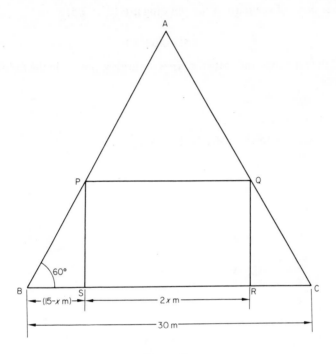

Fig. 4.13

Let PQRS represent the plan of the building, with length SR $= 2x$ m. Hence

$$BS = (15 - x) \text{ m} \quad \text{and} \quad PS = (15 - x) \tan 60°$$

$$\text{Area PQRS} = 2x(15 - x) \tan 60°$$

$$= 2x(15 - x)\sqrt{3}$$

$$= x \, 30\sqrt{3} - x^2 2\sqrt{3}$$

$$\therefore \frac{dA}{dx} = 30\sqrt{3} - 2x \, 2\sqrt{3}$$

$$\therefore \frac{d^2A}{dx^2} = -4\sqrt{3}$$

Let $dA/dx = 0$

$$\therefore \ 30\sqrt{3} - 4x\sqrt{3} = 0$$

$$\therefore \ x = \frac{30\sqrt{3}}{4\sqrt{3}} = 7.5$$

Dimensions of the plan of the building are $15 \times 7.5\sqrt{3}$ m.

EXERCISE 4.1

Find the positions and state the types of turning-points on the following curves.

1. $y = 3x^2 - 6x + 2$

2. $y = 12 + x - x^2$

3. $y = 2x^3 - 15x^2 + 36x + 2$

4. $y = \dfrac{x^3 + 32}{x^2}$

5. $y = 4x + \dfrac{1}{x}$

6. $y = 9x - 3x^2 - x^3 + 3$

7. $y = \dfrac{2\sqrt{x^3}}{3} - 2\sqrt{x}$

8. $y = \dfrac{2x^{3/2}}{9} - x + 2$

9. Find the maximum value of the function $4x - x^2$.

10. Find the maximum and minimum values of the function $x^3 - 12x + 3$.

11. A body moves s m in t sec, and

$$s = at^2 + 2bt + c$$

where a, b, and c are constants. Given that the body starts with velocity 10 m/sec, has a constant acceleration of 12 m/sec^2, and in 1 sec it is 20 m from some fixed point O, calculate the values of a, b, and c.

12. A body moves s m in t sec and

$$s = t^3 - 4t^2 + 4t + 2$$

Calculate, (a) the times when the body is stationary, and (b) the acceleration at these times.

13. A shell fired from the ground rises h m in t sec and

$$h = 100t - 16t^2$$

Calculate (a) its velocity on leaving the ground, (b) the time when the height is a maximum, (c) the maximum height reached, (d) the velocity with which it strikes the ground.

14. Find the x co-ordinates of the turning-points on the graph of,

$$y = \frac{x^3}{3} - \frac{7x^2}{2} + 10x + 1$$

15. Find the maximum and minimum values of,

$$y = 2x^3 + \frac{7x^2}{2} - 20x + 2$$

16. The graph of

$$y = \frac{x^3}{3} - \frac{x^2}{2}(2a - 1) - 2ax + 2$$

has one turning point at $x = 6$. Calculate the value of the constant a.

17. Find the minimum value of the function $12x^2 + 3/x$.

18. If $s = 3 \sin t + 4 \cos t$ where t is in radians, find the smallest positive value of t for which s has a maximum value.

19. Find the maximum and minimum turning-points on the graph of $y = x^2 e^x$.

20. A ladder 20 m long stands on horizontal ground against a vertical wall. If the foot of the ladder slides away from the wall, show that the maximum area will be enclosed by the ladder, ground and wall, when the foot is $10\sqrt{2}$ m from the wall.

21.

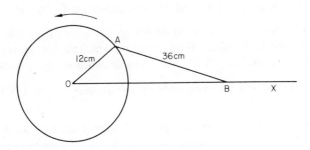

Fig. 4.14

A wheel has a crank OA 12 cm. long and a connecting rod 36 cm. long, the end B moving on a fixed guide OX. Calculate the maximum area of the triangle OAB.

22. The total surface area of a solid cylinder is 100π cm². Calculate the dimensions for the volume to be a maximum.

23. (a) If $y = x^2 + 16/x$, derive an expression for dy/dx from first principles. Sketch the graph of the original function, clearly indicating on the graph where $x = 0$.

   (b) An alternating voltage $v = v_0 \cos \omega t$ is applied across a capacitor of capacitance C farad. Derive an expression for the charging current $C\, dv/dt$ at any instant in terms of v_0, ω, C, and t, and state the peak value of this current.

   C.G.L.I. T.T.

24. If $y = \sin 3\theta$ write down $dy/d\theta$.

25. If $y = 2 \cos 4\theta$ write down $dy/d\theta$.

26. If $i = 100 \sin 100t$ write down di/dt.

27. If $v = 50 \sin 200t$ write down dv/dt.

28. If $i = I_m \sin 2\pi f t$ write down di/dt.

29. An alternating voltage is given by $v = 20 \sin 50t$. Calculate the rate at which the voltage is changing when $t = 0\cdot1$ sec.

30. An alternating current is given by $i = 100 \sin 200t$. Calculate the rate at which the current is changing when $t = 0\cdot01$ sec.

31. An alternating voltage given by $v = 50 \sin 100t$ is applied to a capacitor of 100 μF. Calculate the value of the current after $0\cdot02$ sec.

32. An alternating current given by $i = 40 \sin 30t$ is applied to an inductor of 50 μH. Calculate the induced e.m.f. after $0\cdot01$ sec.

33. Draw the graph of $v = 10 \sin 40t$ for values of t from 0 to $0\cdot16$ sec at intervals of $0\cdot02$ sec. Find the rate at which the voltage is changing after (a) $0\cdot02$ sec, (b) $0\cdot12$ sec, (i) by drawing, (ii) by calculation.

34. (a) From first principles obtain the expression for dy/dx if $y = 5x^2 - 7/x$.

   (b) A circuit contains inductance L henrys and resistance R ohms in series. At an instant t sec the current in amperes through this circuit is $i = 4 \sin \omega t$. To overcome the back e.m.f. due to the inductance, a voltage $L\,di/dt$ is required. Write down an expression for the total voltage across the circuit at this instant. If $\omega = 3000$, $L = 5 \times 10^{-3}$, $R = 10$, sketch a graph showing this voltage, displaying two complete alternations.

C.G.L.I. T.T.

35. (a) Derive from first principles an expression for dy/dx given $y = 3x^2 + 4/x$.

(b) The induced e.m.f. e volts produced at any instant when an alternating current i amperes is flowing in an inductance L henrys is given by $e = -L\,di/dt$. Write expressions for i and e at any instant t sec, for a 50 Hz current of peak value 30 mA flowing in an inductance of 3·2 mH. What is the peak e.m.f. induced? Note, not given in examination; assume current alternating sinusoidally.

C.G.L.I. T.T.

5. Integration

5.1 Integration

In chapter 3 we have studied the process of differentiation, which, starting from a given curve and its equation, leads us to the gradient of the curve at any point, the gradient being represented by the slope of the tangent at each point. It is reasonable to enquire whether this process is reversible; in other words, given the gradient at any point, can we deduce the shape of the curve or its equation? There is such a process to which is given the name 'integration', which has the common meaning of making a complete whole.

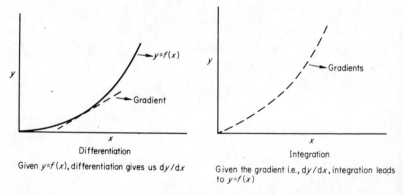

Differentiation

Given $y=f(x)$, differentiation gives us dy/dx

Integration

Given the gradient i.e., dy/dx, integration leads to $y=f(x)$

Fig. 5.1

The reversible nature of this process is of considerable assistance in finding a suitable method of integration; for example, if $dy/dx = 4x^3$, we are able to recognize that the original function representing the curve is $y = x^4$ since the differential coefficient of x^4 is $4x^3$. Furthermore, since a simple rule for differentiation of functions of the type x^n exists, we can obtain our answer by reversing this rule.

Differentiation. Multiply by the power and take 1 from the power.

Integration. Add 1 to the power and divide by the new power.

Example 5.1. If

$$\frac{dy}{dx} = x^2$$

$$\text{then } y = \frac{x^3}{3}$$

Example 5.2. If

$$\frac{dy}{dx} = x^{1/2}$$

$$\text{then } y = \frac{2x^{3/2}}{3}$$

The sign used for the process of integration is an elongated 's' written $\int$, meaning 'summation'. Using this sign, a more complete statement of Example 5.1 would be as follows:

If

$$\frac{dy}{dx} = x^2 \tag{5.1}$$

$$\text{then } dy = x^2 \, dx \tag{5.2}$$

$$\therefore \int dy = \int x^2 \, dx \tag{5.3}$$

$$\therefore y = \frac{x^3}{3} \tag{5.4}$$

The stages (5.1) to (5.4) are illustrated in Fig. 5.2.

(5.1) $\dfrac{dy}{dx} = \tan \psi$

(5.2) $dy = \tan \psi \, dx$

(5.3) $\int dy$ means the summation of an infinite number of small changes in y, such as PQ, P_1Q_1, etc.

(5.4) The final result of this summation reconstructs the curve $y = x^3/3$.

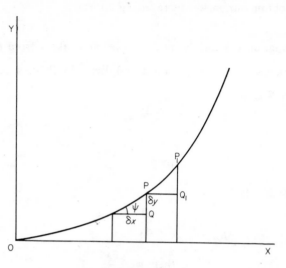

Fig. 5.2

A word of caution is appropriate at this point. The reversible nature of this first rule of differentiation applies only to functions of the type x^n. It is true in general however, that an integral can be considered as 'that function, which when differentiated leads to the given function'. Hence

$$\int F(x)\, \mathrm{d}x = f(x) \quad \text{if} \quad \frac{\mathrm{d}[f(x)]}{\mathrm{d}x} = F(x)$$

5.2 Constant of integration

Suppose the gradient at any point of a curve is given. There will be any number of equal gradients as parts of other curves all of which will be parallel. The only distinguishing features of these curves are their intercepts c_1, c_2, etc., as in Fig. 5.3.

Equation of curve	Gradient, $\mathrm{d}y/\mathrm{d}x$
$y = x^3$	$3x^2$
$y = x^3 + 5$	$3x^2$
$y = x^3 - 2$	$3x^2$

In each case then, integration applied to dy/dx would lead to $y = x^3$, since the constants 5 and -2 do not identify themselves in dy/dx. The possibility of a constant is allowed for by writing $y = x^3 + C$.

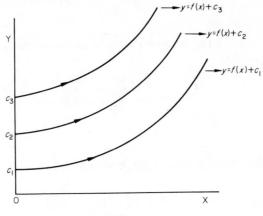

Fig. 5.3

This constant will fall into one of three categories.
(a) It may not be possible to find its value, in this case it remains as $+C$.
(b) It may become zero by subtraction of an equal constant.
(c) Further information about the curve may allow its value to be found.

Example 5.3. Integrate $2x^5$.

$$I = \int 2x^5 \, dx$$

$$\therefore I = \frac{2x^6}{6} + C$$

$$\therefore I = \frac{x^6}{3} + C$$

Example 5.4. Given that the gradient at all points on a curve is $4x - 2$, and that the point $(2,1)$ lies on the curve, find its equation.

$$\frac{dy}{dx} = 4x - 2$$

$$\therefore dy = (4x - 2) \, dx$$

$$\therefore \int dy = \int (4x - 2)\, dx$$

$$\therefore y = \frac{4x^2}{2} - 2x + C$$

Since the point (2, 1) lies on the curve, its co-ordinates must satisfy this last equation.

$$\therefore 1 = \frac{4(2)^2}{2} - 2(2) + C$$

$$\therefore C = -3$$

Therefore the equation of the curve is $y = 2x^2 - 2x - 3$.

Example 5.5. If $d^2y/dx^2 = 2x + 3$ and $dy/dx = 2$ when $x = 1$ and $y = 2$ when $x = 2$, find y in terms of x.

The given function, d^2y/dx^2, represents two steps of differentiation from the equation of the curve; two steps of integration will therefore be required involving two constants, C and K.

$$\frac{d^2y}{dx^2} = 2x + 3$$

$$\therefore \frac{dy}{dx} = x^2 + 3x + C$$

At $x = 1$,

$$\frac{dy}{dx} = 2$$

$$\therefore 2 = 1 + 3 + C$$

$$\therefore -2 = C$$

$$\therefore \frac{dy}{dx} = x^2 + 3x - 2$$

$$\therefore \int dy = \int (x^2 + 3x - 2)\, dx$$

$$\therefore y = \frac{x^3}{3} + \frac{3x^2}{2} - 2x + K$$

At $x = 2$,

$$y = 2$$

$$\therefore \ 2 = \frac{2^3}{3} + \frac{3(2)^2}{2} - 2(2) + K$$

$$\therefore \ 2 = \frac{8}{3} + 6 - 4 + K$$

$$\therefore \ -\frac{8}{3} = K$$

$$\therefore \ y = \frac{x^3}{3} + \frac{3x^2}{2} - 2x - \frac{8}{3}$$

Example 5.6. Write down the general solution of the differential equation, $d^2y/dx^2 = x - 1$.

$$\frac{d^2y}{dx^2} = x - 1$$

$$\therefore \ \frac{dy}{dx} = \frac{x^2}{2} - x + C$$

$$\therefore \ y = \frac{x^3}{6} - \frac{x^2}{2} + Cx + K$$

Example 5.7. At all points on a curve, $d^2y/dx^2 = 12x^2$. Find the equation of the curve if it passes through the points $(1, 6)$ and $(-1, 0)$.

$$\frac{d^2y}{dx^2} = 12x^2$$

$$\therefore \ \frac{dy}{dx} = \frac{12x^3}{3} + C$$

$$\therefore \ y = x^4 + Cx + K$$

At $x = 1$, $y = 6$

$$\therefore \ 6 = 1 + C + K$$

At $x = -1$, $y = 0$

$$\therefore \ 0 = 1 - C + K$$

Solving these equations simultaneously,

$$C = 3 \quad \text{and} \quad K = 2$$

The equation of the curve is $y = x^4 + 3x + 2$.

Example 5.8. A moving object starts with a velocity of 10 m/s and its acceleration after t sec is given by $a = 3 - 2t$. Find the distance travelled when the object first comes to rest.

$$a = \frac{d^2s}{dt^2} = 3 - 2t$$

$$\therefore \; v = \frac{ds}{dt} = 3t - t^2 + C$$

Since the object starts with a velocity of 10 m/s then $v = 10$ when $t = 0$.

$$\therefore \; 10 = 0 - 0 + C$$
$$= C$$
$$\therefore \; v = 3t - t^2 + 10$$

For the object to come to rest, put $v = 0$.

$$\therefore \; 3t - t^2 + 10 = 0$$
$$\therefore \; t^2 - 3t - 10 = 0$$
$$\therefore \; (t - 5)(t + 2) = 0$$
$$\therefore \; t = 5 \qquad (\text{or} -2)$$

From $v = 3t - t^2 + 10$

$$s = \int (3t - t^2 + 10) \, dt$$

$$\therefore \; s = \frac{3t^2}{2} - \frac{t^3}{3} + 10t + K$$

Unless the question gives some particular starting point, it is usual at this stage to assume that at $t = 0$, $s = 0$; it follows therefore that $K = 0$.

$$\therefore \; s = \frac{3t^2}{2} - \frac{t^3}{3} + 10t$$

At $t = 5$,
$$s = \frac{3(5)^2}{2} - \frac{5^3}{3} + 10(5)$$

$$= \frac{75}{2} - \frac{125}{3} + 50$$

$$= 45 \cdot 8 \text{ m}$$

EXERCISE 5.1

Evaluate the following integrals.

1. $\int (1 - 2x + 3x^2)\,dx$

2. $\int (3x + 2)(4x - 1)\,dx$

3. $\int \frac{1}{x^3}\,dx$

4. $\int \sqrt{x^3}\,dx$

5. $\int \frac{2x^5 - 3x^4 + x^3}{x^2}\,dx$

6. $\int \sqrt{x}(3x - x^2)\,dx$

7. $\int (ax + b)(cx - d)\,dx$

8. $\int \left(\frac{p}{x^2} - \frac{q}{x^3}\right) dx$

9. $\int (\pi r^2 - 2\pi r h)\,dr$

10. $\int \left(\frac{1}{\sqrt{t}} - \frac{2}{t^2}\right) dt$

11. $\int \frac{1}{n + 1} x^n\,dx$

12. $\int x^{1/n}\,dx$

13. $\int (E - iR)\,di$

14. $\int CV\,dV$

15. $\int LI\,dI$

16. $\int \frac{x^2 - x - 6}{x - 3}\,dx$

17. $\int 2\pi \sqrt{\frac{l}{g}}\,dl$

18. $\int (r^2 - x^2)\,dx$

19. $\int (1 - \theta + 3\theta^2)\,d\theta$

20. $\int \frac{\pi h}{3}(R^2 + R + 2r)\,dr$

Questions 21 to 25 give the gradients of curves at all points, and the co-ordinates of a point on each curve; find the equations of the curves.

21. $dy/dx = 3x - 2$ $\qquad\qquad y = 2, \quad x = 1$

22. $ds/dt = t - t^2 + 1$ $\qquad\quad s = 3, \quad t = 2$

23. $dh/dt = 3/\sqrt{t} + \sqrt{t}$ $\qquad h = 1, \quad t = 4$

24. $dv/dt = (1 - t)(1 + t)$ $\qquad v = 3, \quad t = 2$

25. $di/dt = (3t + 2)(\sqrt{t} + 1)$ $\qquad i = 2, \quad t = 1$

26. Given $d^2y/dx^2 = 2 - x$, and when $x = 1$, $dy/dx = 2$, and $y = 3$, find the equation of the curve.

27. Given $d^2s/dt^2 = t^3 - 3t^2 + 4$, and the curve passes through the points ($t = 1$, $s = 2$) and ($t = 2$, $s = 3$), find $s = f(t)$.

28. The velocity of a body after t sec is given by $v = t + 4$. Calculate the distance travelled in the first 3 sec.

29. A body starts with a velocity of 10 m/sec and its acceleration after t sec is given by $a = 1 + t + t^2$. Find its velocity after 2 sec.

30. A stone falling from rest is accelerated by the force of gravity, $g = 9.75$ m/sec^2. Calculate the distance through which it falls during the 4th second.

31. A shell projected upwards with an initial velocity of 500 m/sec is decelerated by the force of gravity. Calculate (a) its maximum height, and (b) its height above the ground after 10 sec.

32. The velocity of a body is given by $v = 12 - 4t$. Calculate the velocity with which it returns to the starting point.

33. The brakes of a train have a retarding effect given by $a = -5 - t$. The velocity when the brakes are applied is 28 m/sec. Calculate the distance travelled before the train is halted.

34. The angular velocity of a wheel is given by $d\theta/dt = 1 + t$, where θ is in radians and t in seconds. If $\theta = 0$ when $t = 0$, calculate the time when the wheel has turned through π radians.

5.3   Definite integrals

In the examples in section 5.2, we have reached a general relationship connecting y and x for all values of x. This present section is concerned with the result of integration over a limited range of the graph; the limits are generally represented by two values of x.

Example 5.9. Given $dy/dx = 3x + 2$, find the change in y as x changes from 1 to 3.

$$\frac{dy}{dx} = 3x + 2$$

$$\therefore \int dy = \int_1^3 (3x + 2)\, dx$$

$$\therefore y = \left[\frac{3x^2}{2} + 2x + C \right]_1^3$$

The expression within the brackets is the graphical function and substitution of 3 for x will give the length of ordinate, y_3, and 1 for x will give y_1. Hence, the change in y is $y_3 - y_1$.

$$\therefore \; y_3 - y_1 = \left[\frac{3(3)^2}{2} + 2(3) + C\right] - \left[\frac{3(1)^2}{2} + 2(1) + C\right]$$

$$= 19\tfrac{1}{2} + C - 3\tfrac{1}{2} - C = 16$$

In this type of integral, the constant terms $+C$ and $-C$ cancel; it is unnecessary, therefore, to include the constant in the calculation.

5.4 Area bounded by a curve, the x-axis, and the lines $x = a$ and $x = b$

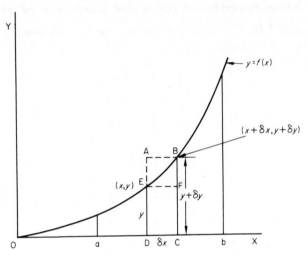

Fig. 5.4

Points $E(x, y)$ and $B(x + \delta x, y + \delta y)$ are taken on the curve whose equation is $y = f(x)$. We consider the area of the strip BCDE. This area lies between the two rectangles ABCD and EFCD.

The area lies between the values

$$\delta x(y + \delta y) \text{ and } y\,\delta x$$

The area lies between the values

$$(y\,\delta x + \delta x\,\delta y) \text{ and } y\,\delta x.$$

But as δx and $\delta y \to 0$, then $\delta x\,\delta y$ becomes infinitely small and can be neglected.

$$\therefore \; \text{Area BCDE lies between } y\,\delta x \text{ and } y\,\delta x$$
$$\therefore \; \text{Area} = y\,\delta x$$

The complete area between the lines $x = a$ and $x = b$ is composed of an infinite number of such strips whose areas are added by the process of integration.

$$\therefore A = \int_a^b y \, dx$$

$$= \int_a^b f(x) \, dx$$

The following conditions must apply to the use of this formula; (a) the x-axis must be a boundary, (b) the limits a and b must be values of x.

Example 5.10. Calculate the area bounded by the curve $y = x^2$, the x-axis and the lines $x = 1$ and $x = 3$.

$$A = \int_a^b f(x) \, dx$$

$$= \int_1^3 x^2 \, dx$$

$$= \left[\frac{x^3}{3} \right]_1^3$$

$$= \left[\frac{3^3}{3} \right] - \left[\frac{1^3}{3} \right]$$

$$= 8\tfrac{2}{3} \text{ sq. units}$$

Example 5.11. Calculate the area bounded by the curve

$$y = x^2 - 5x + 6$$

and the x-axis.

Since the limits are not given, the curve and the x-axis must be sufficient boundaries to enclose the required area; in other words, the curve intersects the x-axis and the area lies between them. The function is identified as a quadratic, the graph of which is a parabola.

The area required is shown shaded in Fig. 5.5 between the values of x at A and B; these values will be the limits of integration.

On the x-axis,

$$y = 0$$

$$\therefore \text{ let } x^2 - 5x + 6 = 0$$

$$\therefore (x - 2)(x - 3) = 0$$

$$\therefore x = 2 \text{ or } 3$$

$$\therefore A = \int_2^3 (x^2 - 5x + 6) \, dx$$

$$= \left[\frac{x^3}{3} - \frac{5x^2}{2} + 6x \right]_2^3$$

$$= \left[\frac{3^3}{3} - \frac{5(3)^2}{2} + 6(3) \right] - \left[\frac{2^3}{3} - \frac{5(2)^2}{2} + 6(2) \right]$$

$$= [9 - 22\tfrac{1}{2} + 18] - [2\tfrac{2}{3} - 10 + 12]$$

$$= 4\tfrac{1}{2} - 4\tfrac{2}{3}$$

$$= -\tfrac{1}{6} \text{ sq. units}$$

The student need not concern himself, at this stage, with the conventions of positive and negative areas.

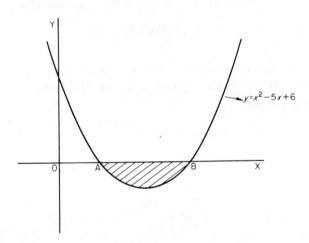

Fig. 5.5

Example 5.12. Draw on graph paper, the graph of $y = 8x - x^2$ for values of x from 0 to 8. Calculate the area bounded by the curve and the x-axis, (a) by mid-ordinate rule, (b) by Simpson's rule, (c) by integration.

$$y = 8x - x^2$$

x:	0	1	2	3	4	5	6	7	8
y:	0	7	12	15	16	15	12	7	0

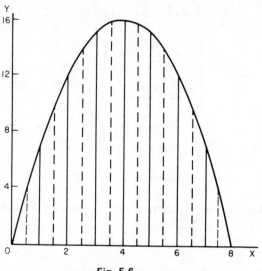

Fig. 5.6

Ordinates, shown by a full line are erected at integral values of x; mid-ordinates, shown broken at values of $x = \frac{1}{2}$, $1\frac{1}{2}$, $2\frac{1}{2}$, etc.

(a) Mid-ordinate rule

$$\text{Average of mid-ordinates} = \frac{(3\cdot75 + 9\cdot55 + 13\cdot75 + 15\cdot75) \times 2}{8}$$

$$= \frac{85\cdot6}{8}$$

$$\therefore \text{ Area} = \frac{85\cdot6}{8} \times 8$$

$$= 85\cdot6 \text{ sq. units}$$

(b) Simpson's rule

$$\text{Area} = \frac{1}{3}\left[0 + 0 + 4\begin{pmatrix}7\\15\\15\\7\end{pmatrix} + 2\begin{pmatrix}12\\16\\12\end{pmatrix}\right]$$

$$= \frac{1}{3}\left[176 + 80\right]$$

$$= 85\cdot3 \text{ sq. units}$$

(c) Integration

$$A = \int_0^8 (8x - x^2)\,dx$$

$$= \left[4x^2 - \frac{x^3}{3} \right]_0^8$$

$$= \left[4(8)^2 - \frac{8^3}{3} \right] - 0$$

$$= 85\cdot3 \text{ sq. units}$$

5.5 Mean value and r.m.s. value

In Volume 2, chapter 5, we have used the mid-ordinate rule and Simpson's rule to calculate mean values and r.m.s. values. The use of integration now provides a further method of obtaining these values without the need to draw the graph.

Mean value

$$\text{Mean value} = \frac{\text{area under curve}}{\text{length of base}}$$

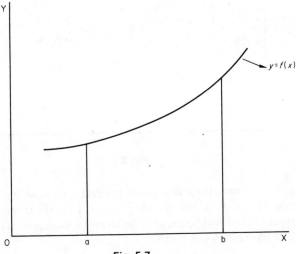

Fig. 5.7

Let the equation of the curve be $y = f(x)$ and the limits along the x-axis, a and b.

$$\therefore\ y_{mean} = \frac{1}{b - a} \int_a^b f(x)\,dx$$

Using the data of Example 5.12

$$y_{mean} = \tfrac{1}{8} \times 85\cdot3 = 10\cdot66$$

R.M.S. value

We must first find the mean, i.e., the average of (ordinates)^2, and then take the square root of this value.

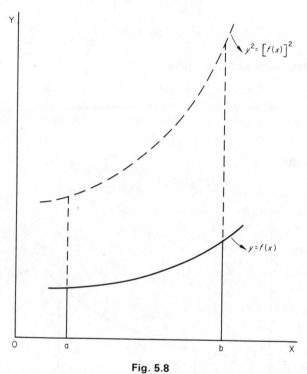

Fig. 5.8

In Fig. 5.8, we imagine a new graph produced by squaring each of the ordinates of $y = f(x)$; the new graph, $y^2 = [f(x)]^2$, is shown broken. The average of y^2 will be the area under this new graph, divided by the length of base along the x-axis.

$$\therefore (y^2)_{mean} = \frac{1}{b-a}\int_a^b [f(x)]^2 \, dx$$

$$\therefore y_{r.m.s.} = \sqrt{\left\{\frac{1}{(b-a)}\int_a^b [f(x)]^2 \, dx\right\}}$$

Using the data of Example 5.12,

$$\therefore\ y_{\text{r.m.s.}} = \sqrt{\left\{\frac{1}{8}\int_0^8 (8x - x^2)^2\,\mathrm{d}x\right\}}$$

$$= \sqrt{\left\{\frac{1}{8}\int_0^8 (64x^2 - 16x^3 + x^4)\,\mathrm{d}x\right\}}$$

$$= \sqrt{\left\{\frac{1}{8}\left[\left(\frac{64x^3}{3}\right) - 4x^4 + \frac{x^5}{5}\right]_0^8\right\}}$$

$$= \sqrt{\left\{\frac{1}{8}\left[\frac{64(8)^3}{3} - 4(8)^4 + \frac{8^5}{5}\right] - 0\right\}}$$

$$= \sqrt{\left\{\frac{1}{8} \times 8^3\left[\frac{64}{3} - 4 \times 8 + \frac{8^2}{5}\right]\right\}}$$

$$= \sqrt{\{8^2[21{\cdot}33 - 32 + 12{\cdot}8]\}}$$

$$= 8\sqrt{2{\cdot}13}$$

$$= 8 \times 1{\cdot}459$$

$$= 11{\cdot}7$$

Comparing this result with that obtained by using Simpson's rule, the following figures emerge.

x:	0	1	2	3	4	5	6	7	8
y:	0	7	12	15	16	15	12	7	0
y^2:	0	49	144	225	256	225	144	49	0

$$\text{Area} = \frac{1}{3}\left[0 + 0 + 4\begin{pmatrix}49\\225\\225\\49\end{pmatrix} + 2\begin{pmatrix}144\\256\\144\end{pmatrix}\right]$$

$$= \frac{1}{3}[4 \times 548 + 2 \times 544]$$

$$= \frac{3280}{3}$$

$$\therefore\ (y^2)_{\text{mean}} = \frac{3280}{3 \times 8}$$

$$\therefore\ y_{\text{r.m.s.}} = \sqrt{136{\cdot}6}$$

$$= 11{\cdot}69$$

This result compares very favourably with that obtained by integral calculus. This close correlation can be expected when the degree of the graphical function is not higher than 2, i.e., x^2.

EXERCISE 5.2

Evaluate the definite integrals in questions 1 to 5.

1. $\displaystyle\int_1^3 (x + 5)(2 - x)\,dx$

2. $\displaystyle\int_1^2 \left(t^2 - \frac{1}{t^2}\right) dt$

3. $\displaystyle\int_{-1}^{+1} (3r^2 - 2r - 1)\,dr$

4. $\displaystyle\int_0^4 (\sqrt{x} - 2x^{3/2} + 3)\,dx$

5. $\displaystyle\int_{-1/2}^{+1/2} \frac{x(1 - x)(1 + x)}{x^5}\,dx$

Calculate the areas bounded by the given curves, the x-axis and the given ordinates. Questions 6 to 10.

6. $y = 4x^2 - 3x$ $x = 1$, $x = 3$

7. $y = \dfrac{1}{x^2}$ $x = \frac{1}{2}$, $x = 2\frac{1}{2}$

8. $y = \dfrac{1}{\sqrt{x}}$ $x = 1$, $x = 16$

9. $y = (2x - 1)(x + 1)$ $x = -1$, $x = 1$

10. $y = 3x^{-2} - 2x^{-3}$ $x = -1$, $x = 1$

11. Calculate the mean value of the function $y = 4x - x^2$ between the limits $x = 0$ and $x = 4$, (a) by mid-ordinate rule, (b) by Simpson's rule, (c) by integration.

12. Calculate the r.m.s. value of the function $y = x^3$ between the limits $x = 0$ and $x = 4$, (a) by Simpson's rule, (b) by integration.

13. Sketch the graph of $y = x(x - 2)(x + 2)$. Calculate (a) the mean value, (b) the r.m.s. value of the function between the limits $x = -2$ and $x = 2$.

14. Sketch the graph of $y = 3x$. Calculate the mean value of the function between the limits $x = 0$ and $x = 3$. Check your result by a geometrical method.

15. Sketch the graph of $y = (x - 2)^2$ and find the mean value of the function between the limits $x = 0$ and $x = 4$.

5.6 Exponential and logarithmic integration

Integration of e^{kx}

It has been noted in section 5.1 that the mechanical rule for the integration of functions of the type x^n does not apply to any other function. To emphasize this point with regard to the integration of e^{kx}, it is useful to compare the structure of the two functions.

e^{kx} has a constant base and a variable power
x^n has a variable base and a constant power.

We now rely on the general idea, that the processes of differentiation and integration are opposites. We can say that the integral of $f(x)$ is that function which when differentiated results in $f(x)$.

Hence, if $y = e^{kx}$,

$$\frac{dy}{dx} = k\,e^{kx}$$

$$\therefore \int k\,e^{kx}\,dx = e^{kx}$$

$$\therefore \int e^{kx}\,dx = \frac{1}{k}\,e^{kx} \tag{5.5}$$

Integration of $1/(ax + b)$

If $y = \log(ax + b)$,

$$\frac{dy}{dx} = \frac{a}{ax + b}$$

$$\therefore \int \frac{a\,dx}{ax + b} = \log(ax + b)$$

$$\therefore \int \frac{1\,dx}{ax + b} = \frac{1}{a}\log(ax + b) \tag{5.6}$$

Note. In e^{kx}, the power is a linear function of x, and in $1/(ax + b)$, the denominator is also a linear function of x. The differential coefficients k and a respectively, appear as divisors in the integrals.

Find the general solutions of the following integrals.

Example 5.13.

(a) $\displaystyle \int e^{2x}\,dx$,   (b) $\displaystyle \int (1 - e^{-Rt/L})\,dt$,   (c) $\displaystyle \int \frac{E}{R}\,e^{-t/CR}\,dt$

(a) $\int e^{2x}\,dx = \dfrac{1}{2}e^{2x} + k$

(b) $\int (1 - e^{-Rt/L})\,dt = t + \dfrac{L}{R}e^{-Rt/L} + k$

(c) $\int \dfrac{E}{R}e^{-t/CR}\,dt = -EC\,e^{-t/CR} + k$

Example 5.14

    (a) $\int \dfrac{1}{3x}\,dx$,   (b) $\int \dfrac{1}{3x - 2}\,dx$,   (c) $\int \dfrac{1}{V - iR}\,di$

(a) $\int \dfrac{1}{3x}\,dx = \int \dfrac{1}{3}\left(\dfrac{1}{x}\right)dx = \dfrac{1}{3}\log x + k$

(b) $\int \dfrac{1}{3x - 2}\,dx = \dfrac{1}{3}\log (3x - 2) + k$

(c) $\int \dfrac{1}{V - iR}\,di = -\dfrac{1}{R}\log (V - iR) + k$

Example 5.15. The growth of current in an inductive circuit.

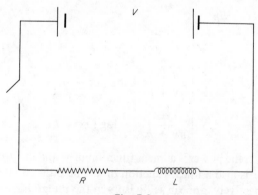

Fig. 5.9

The total applied voltage is balanced by the p.d. across the resistance R and the induced e.m.f. in the inductance L.

$$\therefore\; V = Ri + L\dfrac{di}{dt}$$

$$\therefore \ V - Ri = L\frac{di}{dt}$$

$$\therefore \ (V - Ri)\,dt = L\,di$$

$$\therefore \ \frac{1}{L}\,dt = \frac{1}{V - Ri}\,di$$

Integrating both sides of this function,

$$\frac{t}{L} = -\frac{1}{R}\log\,(V - Ri) + K_1$$

$$\therefore \ -\frac{Rt}{L} = \log\,(V - Ri) + K_2,$$

where $K_2 = -RK_1$.

At the instant of closing the switch, i.e., at $t = 0$, then $i = 0$.

$$\therefore \ 0 = \log V + K_2$$

$$\therefore \ -\log V = K_2$$

$$\therefore \ -\frac{Rt}{L} = \log\,(V - Ri) - \log V$$

$$= \log\left(\frac{V - Ri}{V}\right)$$

Using the definition of a logarithm,

$$e^{-Rt/L} = \frac{V - Ri}{V}$$

$$\therefore \ V\,e^{-Rt/L} = V - Ri$$

$$\therefore \ Ri = V(1 - e^{-Rt/L})$$

$$\therefore \ i = \frac{V}{R}(1 - e^{-Rt/L})$$

$$= I(1 - e^{-Rt/L})$$

where I is the final current.

Example 5.16. Calculate the area bounded by the curve $y = 4e^{3x}$, the x- and y-axes, and the line $x = 1$.

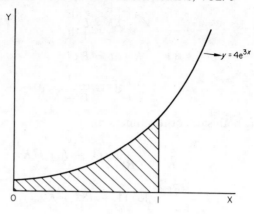

Fig. 5.10

The lower limit of integration is $x = 0$, representing the y-axis.

$$\therefore A = \int_0^1 4\,e^{3x}\,dx$$

$$= \left[\frac{4\,e^{3x}}{3}\right]_0^1$$

$$= \frac{4\,e^3}{3} - \frac{4\,e^0}{3}$$

$$= \frac{4 \times 20 \cdot 1}{3} - \frac{4}{3}$$

$$= 25 \cdot 5 \text{ sq. units}$$

Example 5.17. Calculate the area bounded by the curve $y = 3/(2x - 1)$, the x-axis, and the lines $x = 1$ and $x = 3$.

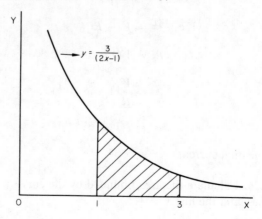

Fig. 5.11

$$A = \int_1^3 \frac{3}{2x - 1} \, dx$$

$$= \left[\frac{3}{2} \log (2x - 1) \right]_1^3$$

$$= \left[\frac{3}{2} \log 5 \right] - \left[\frac{3}{2} \log 1 \right]$$

$$= \frac{3}{2} \times 1\cdot6094 - 0$$

$$= 2\cdot41 \text{ sq. units}$$

Example 5.18. In a d.c. circuit containing resistance and inductance, the current iA after t sec is given by $i = (E/R)(1 - e^{-Rt/L})$. Sketch the graph of i against t and interpret the meaning of an area under the graph. If $R = 10 \, \Omega$, $E = 20 \, V$, and $L = 4 \, mF$, calculate the value of the area under the graph from $t = 0$ to $t = 0\cdot001$ sec.

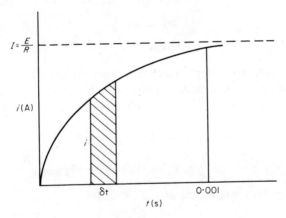

Fig. 5.12

Area shaded $= i \times \delta t$. Since current is rate of transfer of charge, then $i = dq/dt$.

Hence $i \, dt = dq$ or $i \times \delta t = \delta q$.

Hence the shaded area represents the amount of charge transferred in time δt and the total area under the graph will represent the total charge transferred between 0 and 0·001 sec.

$$q = \int dq = \int_0^{0\cdot001} i \, dt = \int_0^{0\cdot001} \frac{E}{R}(1 - e^{-Rt/L}) \, dt$$

$$= \int_0^{0\cdot001} \frac{20}{10}(1 - e^{-10t/(4\times10^{-3})}) \, dt$$

$$= \int_0^{0\cdot001} 2(1 - e^{-2500t}) \, dt$$

$$= 2\left[t + \frac{1}{2500} e^{-2500t}\right]_0^{0\cdot001}$$

$$= 2\left[0\cdot001 + \frac{1}{2500} e^{-2\cdot5}\right] - 2\left[0 + \frac{1}{2500}\right]$$

$$= 2\left[0\cdot001 + \frac{1}{2500} \times 0\cdot0821\right] - \frac{1}{1250}$$

$$= 2[0\cdot001 + 0\cdot003284 \times 10^{-2}] - 0\cdot0008$$

$$= 0\cdot002 + 0\cdot006568 \times 10^{-2} - 0\cdot0008$$

$$= 200 \times 10^{-5} + 6\cdot568 \times 10^{-5} - 80 \times 10^{-5}$$

$$= 126\cdot6 \times 10^{-5}$$

$$= 1270 \, \mu C$$

Example 5.19. The energy stored in a charged capacitor.

The current in a d.c. circuit containing capacitance and resistance is given by, $i = (V/R) e^{-t/CR}$, and the p.d. across the capacitor by, $v = V(1 - e^{-t/CR})$.

Hence

$$\text{Power} = i \times v = \frac{V}{R} e^{-t/CR} \times V(1 - e^{-t/CR}) \text{ watts}$$

Energy supplied in time $\delta t = iv \times \delta t$ J

$$= \frac{V^2}{R}(e^{-t/CR} - e^{-2t/CR}) \, \delta t \text{ J}$$

∴ Total energy supplied when capacitor fully charged

$$= \frac{V^2}{R} \int_0^\infty (e^{-t/CR} - e^{-2t/CR}) \, dt \quad \text{J} \tag{5.7}$$

$$= \frac{V^2}{R}\left[-CR \, e^{-t/CR} + \frac{CR}{2} e^{-2t/CR}\right]_0^\infty \quad \text{J}$$

$$= \frac{V^2}{R}\left[-0+0\right] - \frac{V^2}{R}\left[-CR\,e^0 + \frac{CR}{2}\,e^0\right]\ J$$

$$= 0 - \frac{V^2}{R}\left[-CR + \frac{CR}{2}\right]\ J$$

$$= \frac{V^2}{R} \times \frac{CR}{2}\ J$$

$$= \tfrac{1}{2}CV^2\ J$$

Note. Theoretically the capacitor is fully charged only after 'infinite' time; the integral in (5.7) is an interesting application of a definite integral having an upper limit of infinity, ∞.

EXERCISE 5.3

Evaluate the integrals in questions 1 to 10.

1. $\displaystyle\int e^{3x}\,dx$

2. $\displaystyle\int 2\,e^{x/2}\,dx$

3. $\displaystyle\int_0^1 (e^x + e^{-x})\,dx$

4. $\displaystyle\int (e^{0\cdot 1x} + e^{x+a})\,dx$

5. $\displaystyle\int_1^3 \left(\frac{1}{e^{2t}} - \frac{1}{3\,e^{-t}}\right)dt$

6. $\displaystyle\int \frac{1}{3x-2}\,dx$

7. $\displaystyle\int_1^2 \left[\frac{1}{x+1} - \frac{2}{2x-1}\right]dx$

8. $\displaystyle\int_{-1/2}^{-1/4} \frac{10}{1-x}\,dx$

9. $\displaystyle\int \frac{x^2 + 5x + 8}{x+2}\,dx$

10. $\displaystyle\int \frac{6x+4}{x-2}\,dx$

11. Sketch the graph of $y = e^x$ and calculate the area bounded by the curve, the x-axis, and the ordinates $x = 0$ and $x = 2$.

12. Sketch the graph of $y = 1 - e^{-x}$ and calculate the area between the curve, the x-axis, and the ordinates $x = 0$ and $x = 2\cdot 5$.

13. Sketch the graph of $y = 1/x$ and find the mean value of the function between the limits $x = 1$ and $x = 3$.

14. Evaluate $\int_0^1 dx/(5 - 3x)$ and verify the result using Simpson's rule with 5 ordinates.

C.G.L.I. T.T. (part Qn.)

15. The current in a circuit is given by $i = 10\,e^{-2t}$. Calculate the amount of charge transferred between $t = 0$ and $t = 0\cdot 2$ sec.

16. The pressure and volume of a gas may be related by the law $pv = C$. If the work done by the gas in expanding is given by $p\,dv$, calculate the work done in expanding from a volume v_0 to a volume v_1.

17. Find the r.m.s. value of the function $V\,e^{-t/CR}$ from $t = 0$ to $t = CR$, where V, C, and R are constants.

C.G.L.I. T.T. (part Qn.)

18. Find the magnetic energy stored in an inductive circuit of L henrys if the final current is IA.

6. Trigonometry

6.1 Trigonometrical identities; compound angles

Suppose we require to know the relation between the sine of the complete angle $(A + B)$ and the trigonometrical functions of its parts, angle A and angle B.

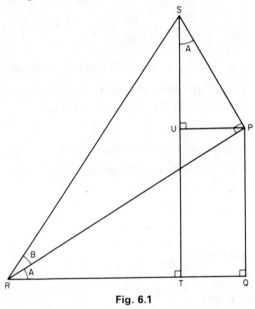

Fig. 6.1

Figure 6.1 shows the angle $(A + B)$ in the right-angled triangle RST, the angle A in the right-angled triangle PQR, and the angle B in the right-angled triangle RSP.

Since $\qquad \angle PRQ = A$

then $\qquad \angle RPQ = (90° - A)$

$$\therefore \ \angle UPR = A$$

$$\therefore \ \angle UPS = (90° - A)$$

$$\therefore \ \angle USP = A$$

In $\triangle RST$, $\qquad \sin(A + B) = \dfrac{TS}{SR} = \dfrac{TU + US}{SR}$

Now $TU = PQ = PR \sin A$ in $\triangle PQR$ and $US = PS \cos A$ in $\triangle USP$

$$\therefore \ \sin(A + B) = \frac{PR \sin A + PS \cos A}{SR}$$

$$= \frac{PR}{SR} \sin A + \frac{PS}{SR} \cos A$$

$$= \cos B \sin A + \sin B \cos A$$

This result, along with others of a similar form, are usually written in a standard pattern as an aid to memorizing them.

(a) $\sin(A + B) = \sin A \cos B + \cos A \sin B$

(b) $\sin(A - B) = \sin A \cos B - \cos A \sin B$

(c) $\cos(A + B) = \cos A \cos B - \sin A \sin B$

(d) $\cos(A - B) = \cos A \cos B + \sin A \sin B$

(e) $\tan(A + B) = \dfrac{\tan A + \tan B}{1 - \tan A \tan B}$

(f) $\tan(A - B) = \dfrac{\tan A - \tan B}{1 + \tan A \tan B}$

6.2 Multiple angles

(g) $\sin 2A$

In (a) above, let $B = A$.

$$\therefore \ \sin(A + A) = \sin A \cos A + \cos A \sin A$$

$$\therefore \ \sin 2A = 2 \sin A \cos A$$

(h) $\cos 2A$

In (c) above let $B = A$.

$$\therefore \ \cos(A + A) = \cos A \cos A - \sin A \sin A$$

$$\therefore \ \cos 2A = \cos^2 A - \sin^2 A$$

There are two other useful forms of this last result, to be obtained by using the identity,

$$\sin^2 A + \cos^2 A = 1$$

They are (i) $\cos 2A = 1 - 2\sin^2 A$

and (j) $\cos 2A = 2\cos^2 A - 1$

6.3 $a\sin\theta + b\cos\theta = R\sin(\theta + \phi)$

The expansions (a) to (d) have useful applications in vectorial addition, a subject which has already been introduced in Volume 2.

Let us consider the expression $3\sin\theta + 4\cos\theta$. We can obtain a result, working from first principles, by drawing the graphs of $y = 3\sin\theta$ and $y = 4\cos\theta$ on the same scale and axes. By the addition

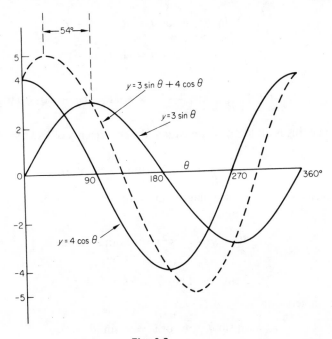

Fig. 6.2

of ordinates at several values of θ we should obtain a series of points from which could be drawn the graph of $3\sin\theta + 4\cos\theta$ as in Fig. 6.2. Comparing the graph of $y = 3\sin\theta + 4\cos\theta$ with the graph of $3\sin\theta$, we note the following features.

(a) Its shape is that of a sine graph.
(b) Its period is 360° as is that of 3 sin θ.
(c) Its amplitude is 5.
(d) In corresponding significant positions, i.e., maximum, zero, and minimum values, it is clear that the graph of 3 sin θ + 4 cos θ leads the graph of 3 sin θ by 54° approximately; this is true generally at all corresponding positions.

From these four observations, we may deduce that,

$$3 \sin \theta + 4 \cos \theta = 5 \sin (\theta + 54°)$$

The accuracy of the amplitude 5 and the phase angle 54° is limited by the graphical method. An expansion of the type sin $(A + B)$ will enable us to justify our conclusion and to verify the accuracy of the two constants.

Let

$$3 \sin \theta + 4 \cos \theta \equiv R \sin (\theta + \phi)$$

$$\therefore \frac{3}{R} \sin \theta + \frac{4}{R} \cos \theta \equiv \sin (\theta + \phi)$$

$$\therefore \sin \theta \times \frac{3}{R} + \cos \theta \times \frac{4}{R} \equiv \sin \theta \cos \phi + \cos \theta \sin \phi$$

Since this is an identity, we equate the coefficients of like terms.

$$\therefore \frac{3}{R} = \cos \phi \quad \text{and} \quad \frac{4}{R} = \sin \phi$$

which can be expressed diagrammatically as in Fig. 6.3.

Hence

$$R = \sqrt{(3^2 + 4^2)} = 5 \quad \text{and} \quad \tan \phi = \tfrac{4}{3}$$
$$\therefore \phi = 53° 8'$$
$$\therefore 3 \sin \theta + 4 \cos \theta = 5 \sin (\theta + 53° 8')$$

or, in general,

$$a \sin \theta + b \cos \theta = R \sin (\theta + \phi)$$

where $R = \sqrt{(a^2 + b^2)}$ and $\phi = \tan^{-1}(b/a)$.

Note. The verbal meaning of this last statement, using the symbol, 'tan^{-1}', is, 'ϕ is the angle whose tangent is b/a'; we have made ϕ the subject of the relation tan $\phi = b/a$.

Similarly, in respect of the difference between vectors,

$$a \sin \theta - b \cos \theta = R \sin (\theta - \phi)$$

where $R = \sqrt{(a^2 + b^2)}$ and $\phi = \tan^{-1}(b/a)$.

The value of ϕ is the smallest positive value of the angle which satisfies $\phi = \tan^{-1}(b/a)$.

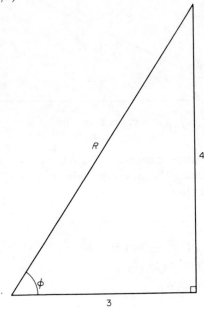

Fig. 6.3

6.4 $a \cos \theta + b \sin \theta = R \cos (\theta - \phi)$

Using the expansion (d) in section 6.1,

$$\frac{a}{R} \cos \theta + \frac{b}{R} \sin \theta \equiv \cos \theta \cos \phi + \sin \theta \sin \phi$$

Equating coefficients of like terms,

$$\left. \begin{array}{l} \dfrac{a}{R} = \cos \phi \\[2em] \dfrac{b}{R} = \sin \phi \end{array} \right\} \text{in diagrammatic form, Fig. 6.4.}$$

Hence $R = \sqrt{(a^2 + b^2)}$, and $\phi = \tan^{-1}(b/a)$.

Similarly,

$$a \cos \theta - b \sin \theta = R \cos (\theta + \phi)$$

where R and ϕ have the same values as previously.

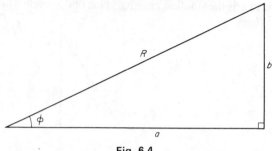

Fig. 6.4

Example 6.1. Alternating currents are given by $i_1 = 10 \sin \omega t$ and $i_2 = 20 \cos \omega t$. Calculate the maximum value of $i_1 + i_2$ and its phase angle of lead referred to i_1.

$$i_1 + i_2 = 10 \sin \omega t + 20 \cos \omega t \equiv R \sin (\omega t + \phi)$$
$$\therefore \ R = \sqrt{(10^2 + 20^2)} = \sqrt{500} = 10\sqrt{5} = 22\cdot36$$
$$\therefore \ \phi = \tan^{-1}(20/10)$$
$$= 63° \ 26'$$

Hence, the maximum value of $i_1 + i_2$ is 22·4 and its phase angle is 63° 26′ leading.

Example 6.2. Alternating voltages are given by $v_1 = 4 \sin \omega t$ and $v_2 = 8 \cos \omega t$. Calculate (a) the amplitude of $v_1 - v_2$, and (b) the value of t in seconds for which $v_1 - v_2 = 4\cdot472$, given that $\omega = 100$ rad/sec.

(a)　　　　　$v_1 - v_2 = 4 \sin \omega t - 8 \cos \omega t \equiv R \sin (\omega t - \phi)$

$$\therefore \ R = \sqrt{(4^2 + 8^2)} = \sqrt{80} = 8\cdot944$$
$$\therefore \ \phi = \tan^{-1}(8/4)$$
$$= 63° \ 26' = 1\cdot1071 \ \text{rad}$$
$$\therefore \ v_1 - v_2 = 8\cdot944 \sin (\omega t - 1\cdot1071)$$

Hence the amplitude of $v_1 - v_2$ is 8·944 V.

(b) Let $8 \cdot 944 \sin (\omega t - 1 \cdot 1071) = 4 \cdot 472$

$$\therefore \sin (\omega t - 1 \cdot 1071) = \frac{4 \cdot 472}{8 \cdot 944} = 0 \cdot 5$$

$$\omega t - 1 \cdot 1071 = \frac{\pi}{6} \quad \text{or} \quad \frac{5\pi}{6}$$

$$\therefore \omega t = \frac{3 \cdot 142}{6} + 1 \cdot 1071 \quad \text{or} \quad \frac{5 \times 3 \cdot 142}{6} + 1 \cdot 1071$$

$$= 1 \cdot 6308 \quad \text{or} \quad 3 \cdot 7254$$

$$\therefore t = 0 \cdot 0163 \quad \text{or} \quad 0 \cdot 0373 \text{ sec}$$

Example 6.3. Alternating currents are given by $i_1 = 40 \sin 50t$ and $i_2 = 30 \cos (50t + \pi/3)$. Express $i_1 + i_2$ in the form $R \sin (50t + \phi)$ and hence solve the equation, $40 \sin 50t + 30 \cos (50t + \pi/3) = 15$.

Before applying the method of Examples 6.1 and 6.2, it will be necessary to express i_2 as a function of the same angle as i_1, i.e., $50t$ radians.

$$i_2 = 30 \cos (50t + \pi/3)$$

$$= 30 \left[\cos 50t \cos \frac{\pi}{3} - \sin 50t \sin \frac{\pi}{3} \right]$$

$$= 30 \left[\frac{1}{2} \cos 50t - \frac{\sqrt{3}}{2} \sin 50t \right]$$

$$= 15 \cos 50t - 15\sqrt{3} \sin 50t$$

$$\therefore i_1 + i_2 = 40 \sin 50t + 15 \cos 50t - 15\sqrt{3} \sin 50t$$

$$= (40 - 15\sqrt{3}) \sin 50t + 15 \cos 50t$$

$$= \sqrt{\{(40 - 15\sqrt{3})^2 + 15^2\}} \sin (50t + \phi)$$

$$\text{where } \phi = \tan^{-1} 15/(40 - 15\sqrt{3})$$

$$= 20 \cdot 5 \sin (50t + 0 \cdot 8168)$$

Let $20 \cdot 5 \sin (50t + 0 \cdot 8168) \quad = 15$.

$$\therefore \sin (50t + 0 \cdot 8168) = \frac{15}{20 \cdot 5} = 0 \cdot 73$$

$$\therefore 50t + 0 \cdot 8168 = 0 \cdot 821 \quad \text{or} \quad (\pi - 0 \cdot 821)$$

$$\therefore 50t = 0 \cdot 821 - 0 \cdot 8168 = 0 \cdot 0042$$

$$\text{or } 50t = 2 \cdot 3210 - 0 \cdot 8168 = 1 \cdot 5042$$

$$\therefore\ t = \frac{0 \cdot 0042}{50} \quad \text{or} \quad \frac{1 \cdot 5042}{50}\ \text{sec}$$

$$\therefore\ t = 0 \cdot 000084 \quad \text{or} \quad 0 \cdot 03008\ \text{sec}$$

Example 6.4. Prove the identity, $\dfrac{\sin 2\theta}{1 + \cos 2\theta} = \tan \theta$.

$$\frac{\sin 2\theta}{1 + \cos 2\theta} = \frac{2 \sin \theta \cos \theta}{1 + 2 \cos^2 \theta - 1}$$

$$= \frac{2 \sin \theta \cos \theta}{2 \cos^2 \theta}$$

$$= \frac{\sin \theta}{\cos \theta}$$

$$= \tan \theta$$

Example 6.5. Solve the equation $4 \sin 2\theta - 2 \cos \theta + 4 \sin \theta - 1 = 0$ for values of θ from $0°$ to $360°$.

$$4 \sin 2\theta - 2 \cos \theta + 4 \sin \theta - 1 = 0$$

$$\therefore\ 4(2 \sin \theta \cos \theta) - 2 \cos \theta + 4 \sin \theta - 1 = 0$$

$$\therefore\ (8 \sin \theta \cos \theta - 2 \cos \theta) + 4 \sin \theta - 1 = 0$$

$$\therefore\ 2 \cos \theta\, (4 \sin \theta - 1) + (4 \sin \theta - 1) = 0$$

$$\therefore\ (4 \sin \theta - 1)(2 \cos \theta + 1) = 0$$

$$\therefore\ \sin \theta = \tfrac{1}{4} \qquad \text{or} \qquad \cos \theta = -\tfrac{1}{2}$$

$$\therefore\ \theta = 14°\ 29', \text{ or } 165°\ 31' \qquad \therefore\ \theta = 120° \text{ or } 240°$$

Example 6.6. Solve the equation $\cos 2\theta + 3 \sin \theta = 2$ for values of θ from $0°$ to $360°$

$$\cos 2\theta + 3 \sin \theta = 2$$

$$\therefore\ 1 - 2 \sin^2 \theta + 3 \sin \theta - 2 = 0$$

$$\therefore\ 2 \sin^2 \theta - 3 \sin \theta + 1 = 0$$

$$\therefore\ (2 \sin \theta - 1)(\sin \theta - 1) = 0$$

$$\sin \theta = \tfrac{1}{2} \qquad \text{or} \qquad \sin \theta = 1$$

$$\therefore\ \theta = 30° \text{ or } 150° \qquad \therefore\ \theta = 90°$$

EXERCISE 6.1

1. Write down the expansions of, (a) $\sin (\omega t + \alpha)$, (b) $\sin (\theta - \beta)$, (c) $\cos (50t + \theta)$, (d) $\cos (2\pi ft - \alpha)$.

2. By considering 75° as (45° + 30°), write down and evaluate in surd form, an expression for (a) sin 75°, (b) cos 75°.

3. Evaluate sin 15° in surd form without the use of tables.

4. Given sin θ = 3/5, write down without the use of tables, the value of (a) sin 2θ, (b) cos 2θ, (c) tan 2θ.

5. Write down the value of tan $22\frac{1}{2}°$ in surd form by means of an expression of the form tan $(A - B)$.

6. Show that

$$\sin \theta + \sin \left(\theta + \frac{\pi}{6} \right) + \sin \left(\theta + \frac{\pi}{3} \right)$$

$$= \frac{1}{2} \left[(3 + \sqrt{3}) \sin \theta + (1 + \sqrt{3}) \cos \theta \right]$$

7. Show that $(\sin A + \cos A)^2 = 1 + \sin 2A$.

8. Show that $\cos 2A = (\cos A + \sin A)(\cos A - \sin A)$.

9. Show that

$$\frac{\tan 2A + \dfrac{\sin A}{\cos 2A}}{\tan 2A - \dfrac{\sin A}{\cos 2A}} = \frac{2 \cos A + 1}{2 \cos A - 1}$$

10. Write $5 \sin \theta + 12 \cos \theta$ in the form $R \sin (\theta + \phi)$, stating the values of R and ϕ.

11. Solve $7 \sin \theta + 24 \cos \theta = 12 \cdot 5$ for values of θ from 0° to 360°.

12. Calculate the maximum value of $4 \sin \omega t + 5 \cos \omega t$.

13. For what value of ωt is $3 \sin \omega t + 2 \cos \omega t$ a maximum?

14. Write $8 \cos \theta - 15 \sin \theta$ as the cosine of a compound angle, evaluating the required constants.

15. Alternating currents are given by $i_1 = 15 \sin \omega t$ and $i_2 = 30 \cos \omega t$. Find by calculation an expression for the value of $i_1 + i_2$.

16. Alternating voltages are given by $v_1 = 50 \sin 10t$ and $v_2 = 75 \cos 10t$, where t is in seconds. Calculate the time when $v_1 + v_2$ first reaches 80 V.

17. (a) State the expansions for $\sin (A - B)$ and $\cos (A + B)$.
    (b) The voltage V between the ends of an a.c. circuit is given by $V = 5 \sin (\omega t - \pi/6) + 7 \cos (\omega t + \pi/4)$. Use the expansions of part (a) above to express V in the form, $A \sin \omega t + B \cos \omega t$. State the values of A and B correct to 3 significant figures.

(c) Sketch, not plot, one complete cycle of the graph of $3 \sin \theta$. On the same set of axes sketch the graph of $\sin 2\theta$ and also the graph of $3 \sin \theta + \sin 2\theta$.

U.E.I.

18. (a) Prove that $\sin (A + B) \sin (A - B) = \sin^2 A - \sin^2 B$.
    (b) Express $\tan A$ in terms of $\tan (A/2) = t$, and hence or otherwise prove that, $2 \cot (A/2) + \tan A = \tan A \cot^2 (A/2)$.
    (c) Give solutions of the equation, $3 \cos \theta - 4 \sin \theta = 5$ for values of θ between $0°$ and $360°$.

C.G.L.I. T.T.

19. Write down the formulae for $\sin (A + B)$ and $\sin (A - B)$ in terms of the trigonometrical ratios for the angles A and B. Hence complete the following identity:

$$\sin 2\pi Ft \times \cos 2\pi ft = \tfrac{1}{2}\left[\sin 2\pi(\ \ )t + \sin 2\pi(\ \ )t\right]$$

E.M.E.U. (part Qn.)

20. Sketch the graph of $i = 30 \sin (\omega t + \pi/6)$ from $t = 0$ to $t = 2\pi/\omega$ sec. If $\omega = 10^3$ rad/sec, state the first instant after $t = 0$, (a) when $i = 0$, (b) when $i = -15$. Also express i in the form,

$$i_1 \sin \omega t + i_2 \cos \omega t$$

C.G.L.I. T.T. (part Qn.)

21. (a) Prove that,

$$\cot \theta - \cot 2\theta = \tan \theta + \cot 2\theta = \operatorname{cosec} 2\theta$$

   (b) Show that, for all values of θ,

$$\sin \theta - \sin \left(\theta + \frac{\pi}{3}\right) + \sin \left(\theta + \frac{2\pi}{3}\right) = 0$$

   (c) Solve the equation, $2 \cos \phi + 5 \sin \phi + 3 = 0$, giving solutions between $-180°$ and $+180°$.

C.G.L.I. T.T.

22. (a) Prove that

$$\frac{\tan A + \tan B}{\tan A - \tan B} = \frac{\sin (A + B)}{\sin (A - B)}$$

   (b) Express $12 \sin \theta - 5 \cos \theta$ in the form $r \cos (\theta + \alpha)$, where r and α are both positive.
   (c) Find the values of θ between $0°$ and $360°$ which satisfy the equation $\sin \theta = 3 \cot \theta$.

C.G.L.I. T.T.

23. (a) Prove the identities,

      (i) $\sin \omega t + \sin (\omega t + 2\pi/3) + \sin (\omega t + 4\pi/3) = 0$

      (ii) $\operatorname{cosec} \theta - \cot \theta = \tan (\theta/2)$

  (b) If $\cot \mu = k$, show that

$$\frac{\sin \theta + k \cos \theta}{\cos \theta - k \sin \theta} = \cot (\mu - \theta)$$

Hence or otherwise, solve the equation,

$$\frac{\sin \theta + 3 \cos \theta}{\cos \theta - 3 \sin \theta} = \sqrt{3}$$

Give solutions between $0°$ and $360°$.

C.G.L.I. T.T.

24. State the expansions of $\cos (A + B)$ and $\sin (A + B)$ in terms of the sines and cosines of A and B. Without using tables, show that $\cos 75° = (\sqrt{3} - 1)/2\sqrt{2}$. If $\cos \phi = 0{\cdot}8$ and ϕ is acute, express $35 \sin (\omega t - \phi)$ in the form $a \sin \omega t + b \cos \omega t$. Sketch the graph of $y = 35 \sin (\omega t - \phi)$ from $t = -2\pi/\omega$ to $t = +2\pi/\omega$.

C.G.L.I. T.T.

25. (a) Expand $\sin 3A$ in terms of powers of $\sin A$.

  (b) Prove that $\dfrac{\sin 3\theta}{1 + 2 \cos 2\theta} = \sin \theta$. Hence or otherwise show that

    $\sin 15° = \dfrac{\sqrt{3} - 1}{2\sqrt{2}}.$

  (c) Calculate the values of ϕ between $-180°$ and $+180°$ which satisfy the equation $5 \cos \phi = 2 + \sin \phi$.

C.G.L.I. T.T.

6.5 Integration of trigonometrical functions

The integration of the trigonometrical functions sine and cosine provides a useful example of the complementary nature of the two processes, differentiation and integration.

(a) $\displaystyle\int \cos \theta \, d\theta$

What function has been differentiated to give $\cos \theta$? Hence

$$\int \cos \theta \, d\theta = \sin \theta \qquad (6.1)$$

(b) $\displaystyle\int \sin\theta \; d\theta$

What function has been differentiated to give $\sin\theta$? Hence

$$\int \sin\theta \; d\theta = -\cos\theta \qquad (6.2)$$

6.6 Multiple and compound angles

$$\int \cos a\theta \; d\theta = \frac{1}{a}\sin a\theta \qquad (6.3)$$

$$\int \sin k\theta \; d\theta = -\frac{1}{k}\cos k\theta \qquad (6.4)$$

$$\int \cos(a\theta + b) \; d\theta = \frac{1}{a}\sin(a\theta + b) \qquad (6.5)$$

$$\int \sin(k\theta + c) \; d\theta = -\frac{1}{k}\cos(k\theta + c) \qquad (6.6)$$

These integrals follow directly from the basic integrals (6.1) and (6.2). It should be noted that the constants a and k in the given functions become divisors in the integrals.

6.7 Integration of $\sin^2\theta$ and $\cos^2\theta$

(a) $\displaystyle\int \sin^2\theta \; d\theta$

It has been emphasized in chapter 4 that the rule for integration of functions of the type x^n does not apply to any other type of function. In order to evaluate the integral of $\sin^2\theta$, we must first express it in one of the basic forms (6.1) or (6.2).

$$\cos 2\theta = 1 - 2\sin^2\theta$$
$$\therefore \; 2\sin^2\theta = 1 - \cos 2\theta$$
$$\therefore \; \sin^2\theta = \frac{1}{2}(1 - \cos 2\theta)$$
$$\therefore \; \int \sin^2\theta \; d\theta = \int \frac{1}{2}(1 - \cos 2\theta) \; d\theta$$
$$= \frac{1}{2}\left(\theta - \frac{\sin 2\theta}{2}\right) \qquad (6.7)$$

(b) $\int \cos^2 \theta \; d\theta$

$$\cos 2\theta = 2 \cos^2 \theta - 1$$

$$\therefore \; \cos^2 \theta = \frac{1}{2}(1 + \cos 2\theta)$$

$$\therefore \; \int \cos^2 \theta \; d\theta = \int \frac{1}{2}(1 + \cos 2\theta) \; d\theta$$

$$= \frac{1}{2}\left(\theta + \frac{\sin 2\theta}{2}\right) \qquad (6.8)$$

Example 6.7. $\quad \displaystyle\int \sin^2 \omega t \; dt = \int \frac{1}{2}(1 - \cos 2\omega t) \; dt$

$$= \frac{1}{2}\left(t - \frac{\sin 2\omega t}{2\omega}\right)$$

Example 6.8. $\quad \displaystyle\int 3 \cos^2 2\pi ft \; dt = 3 \int \frac{1}{2}(1 + \cos 4\pi ft) \; dt$

$$= \frac{3}{2}\left(t + \frac{\sin 4\pi ft}{4\pi f}\right)$$

Example 6.9. $\displaystyle\int \sin^2\left(\omega t + \frac{\pi}{3}\right) dt = \int \frac{1}{2}\left[1 - \cos\left(2\omega t + \frac{2\pi}{3}\right)\right] dt$

$$= \frac{1}{2}\left[t - \frac{\sin\left(2\omega t + \dfrac{2\pi}{3}\right)}{2\omega}\right]$$

Example 6.10. $\displaystyle\int_0^{\pi/3} (\sin 2\theta + 4 \cos^2 \theta) \; d\theta$

$$= \left[-\frac{\cos 2\theta}{2} + \frac{4}{2}\left(\theta + \frac{\sin 2\theta}{2}\right)\right]_0^{\pi/3}$$

$$= \left[-\frac{\cos 2\pi/3}{2} + 2\left(\frac{\pi}{3} + \frac{\sin 2\pi/3}{2}\right)\right] - \left[-\frac{\cos 0}{2} + 2\left(0 + \frac{\sin 0}{2}\right)\right]$$

$$= \frac{1}{4} + 2\left(\frac{\pi}{3} + \frac{\sqrt{3}}{4}\right) + \frac{1}{2}$$

$$= \frac{3}{4} + \frac{2\pi}{3} + \frac{\sqrt{3}}{2}$$

Example 6.11. Find the mean value of the alternating current given by $i = I_m \sin \omega t$ over half a period.

The period of the function is $2\pi/\omega$. Hence

$$\text{Mean value } i = \frac{1}{\pi/\omega} \int_0^{\pi/\omega} I_m \sin \omega t \, dt$$

$$= \frac{\omega}{\pi} \left[-\frac{I_m \cos \omega t}{\omega} \right]_0^{\pi/\omega}$$

$$= -\frac{\omega I_m}{\pi \omega} \left[\cos\left(\omega \frac{\pi}{\omega}\right) - \cos 0 \right]$$

$$= -\frac{I_m}{\pi} \left[-1 - 1 \right]$$

$$= \frac{2}{\pi} I_m$$

Example 6.12. Find the r.m.s. value of an alternating current given by $i = I_m \sin \omega t$ over a whole period.

$$\text{R.M.S. value of } i = \sqrt{\left\{ \frac{1}{2\pi/\omega} \int_0^{2\pi/\omega} I_m{}^2 \sin^2 \omega t \, dt \right\}}$$

$$= \sqrt{\left\{ \frac{\omega I_m{}^2}{2\pi} \int_0^{2\pi/\omega} \tfrac{1}{2}(1 - \cos 2\omega t) \, dt \right\}}$$

$$= \sqrt{\left\{ \frac{\omega I_m{}^2}{4\pi} \left[t - \frac{\sin 2\omega t}{2\omega} \right]_0^{2\pi/\omega} \right\}}$$

$$= \sqrt{\left\{ \frac{\omega I_m{}^2}{4\pi} \left[\frac{2\pi}{\omega} - \frac{\sin(2\omega \times 2\pi/\omega)}{2\omega} \right] - 0 \right\}}$$

$$= \sqrt{\left(\frac{I_m{}^2}{2} - 0 \right)}$$

$$= \frac{I_m}{\sqrt{2}}$$

In Example 6.11, the mean value is taken over half a period, since the value over a whole period is zero due to the symmetrical negative half of the wave-form. The r.m.s. value of i over a half period is unaltered and a comparison of the two results leads to an expression of the 'form factor'.

$$\text{Form factor} = \frac{\text{r.m.s. value}}{\text{mean value}}$$

$$= \frac{I_m}{\sqrt{2}} \times \frac{\pi}{2I_m}$$

$$= 1{\cdot}11$$

The form factor is a measure of the 'peakiness' of the wave, the value $1{\cdot}11$ applying to a sine wave. Values less than $1{\cdot}11$ would represent a flatter wave and those greater than $1{\cdot}11$, a more peaky wave, as for example, a triangular wave.

Example 6.13. Sketch the graph of $y = 5 + 3 \sin 2\omega t$ from $t = 0$ to $t = 2\pi/\omega$. By considering the integral of $(5 + 3 \sin 2\omega t)^2$, find the r.m.s. value of y over the range $t = 0$ to $t = \pi/2\omega$.

C.G.L.I. T.T. (part Qn.)

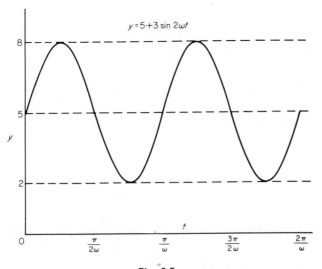

Fig. 6.5

Mean value of y^2 from $t = 0$ to $t = \pi/2\omega$

$$= \frac{1}{\pi/2\omega} \int_0^{\pi/2\omega} (5 + 3 \sin 2\omega t)^2 \, \mathrm{d}t$$

$$= \frac{2\omega}{\pi} \int_0^{\pi/2\omega} (25 + 9 \sin^2 2\omega t + 30 \sin 2\omega t) \, \mathrm{d}t$$

$$= \frac{2\omega}{\pi} \int_0^{\pi/2\omega} \left[25 + 9 \times \tfrac{1}{2}(1 - \cos 4\omega t) + 30 \sin 2\omega t \right] dt$$

$$= \frac{2\omega}{\pi} \left[25t + \frac{9t}{2} - \frac{9}{2} \times \frac{\sin 4\omega t}{4\omega} - \frac{30 \cos 2\omega t}{2\omega} \right]_0^{\pi/2\omega}$$

$$= \frac{2\omega}{\pi} \left[\frac{25\pi}{2\omega} + \frac{9\pi}{4\omega} - \frac{9}{2} \times \frac{\sin 2\pi}{4\omega} - \frac{30 \cos \pi}{2\omega} \right] - \frac{2\omega}{\pi} \left[0 - \frac{30}{2\omega} \right]$$

$$= \frac{2\omega}{\pi} \left[\frac{50\pi + 9\pi + 60}{4\omega} \right] + \frac{30}{\pi}$$

$$= \frac{59}{2} + \frac{60}{\pi}$$

$$\therefore \text{ R.M.S. value of } y = \sqrt{\left(\frac{59}{2} + \frac{60}{\pi} \right)} = 6 \cdot 97$$

EXERCISE 6.2

1. Integrate the following functions
   (a) $3 \sin \theta$
   (b) $2 \cos \theta$
   (c) $\sin 2\theta + \cos 3\theta$
   (d) $\sin (2\theta + \pi)$
   (e) $3 \cos \left(4\theta - \frac{\pi}{2} \right)$
   (f) $50 \sin \omega t$
   (g) $10 \cos 50t$
   (h) $5 \sin 2\pi ft$
   (i) $\sin^2 \omega t$
   (j) $\cos^2 (2\pi ft)$

2. Evaluate the following definite integrals
   (a) $\displaystyle\int_0^{\pi/6} (\sin \theta + \cos \theta) \, d\theta$
   (b) $\displaystyle\int_0^{\pi/3} \sin (2\theta + \pi) \, d\theta$
   (c) $\displaystyle\int_0^{\pi/4} \cos \left(3\theta + \frac{\pi}{2} \right) d\theta$
   (d) $\displaystyle\int_0^{\pi/\omega} \sin^2 \omega t \, dt$
   (e) $\displaystyle\int_0^{\pi/\omega} \cos^2 \omega t \, dt$
   (f) $\displaystyle\int_{\pi/6}^{\pi/3} (\sin \theta - \cos \theta) \, d\theta$
   (g) $\displaystyle\int_0^{0 \cdot 1} \sin (5t + 0 \cdot 2) \, dt$
   (h) $\displaystyle\int_{0 \cdot 1}^{0 \cdot 3} \cos (6t - 0 \cdot 1) \, dt$
   (i) $\displaystyle\int_0^{2\pi/\omega} \sin \omega t \, dt$
   (j) $\displaystyle\int_0^{2\pi/\omega} \cos \omega t \, dt$

3. Find the mean value of the alternating current given by $i = I_m \sin \omega t$ over a half period.

4. Find the r.m.s. value of the alternating voltage given by

$$v = V_m \sin 2\pi f t$$

over a whole period.

5. Given that $i_1 = 10 \sin \omega t$ and $i_2 = 20 \cos \omega t$, find an expression for $i_1 + i_2$ of the form $R \sin (\omega t + \phi)$, and calculate the r.m.s. value of it over a whole period.

6. Given that $v_1 = 5 \cos \omega t$ and $v_2 = 8 \sin (\omega t + \pi/6)$, find an expression for $v_1 + v_2$ and find the mean value of the function over the range, $t = 0$ to $t = \pi/\omega$ sec.

7. The magnitude of an electric current is a measure of the rate at which charge is being transferred; represent this statement by mathematical symbols and processes. Hence find the total electric charge which passes any point in a circuit in which the current is given by $i = 10 \sin 50t$, during the time $t = 0$ to $t = 0.1$ sec.

8. An alternating voltage given by $v = 50 \sin 314t$ is applied to a half-wave rectifier in which the resistance in the forward direction is assumed negligible, and in the reverse direction is assumed infinitely large.

Sketch the voltage wave over two whole periods. If the circuit contains a resistance of 25 Ω in series, calculate the r.m.s. value of the current.

7. Algebra

7.1 Simultaneous equations

Example 7.1. Solve the equations,

$$x + 2y - z = 2 \tag{7.1}$$

$$2x + y + z = 7 \tag{7.2}$$

$$5x + y - 2z = 1 \tag{7.3}$$

The method required is an extension of that used for simultaneous equations with two unknowns, namely, the elimination of one unknown, in this case, repeated for a second unknown. The addition of (7.1) and (7.2) will eliminate z.

$$
\begin{array}{r}
x + 2y - z = 2 \\
2x + y + z = 7 \\
\hline
3x + 3y = 9 \\
x + y = 3
\end{array}
\tag{7.4}
$$

Choosing any other pair of equations from (7.1), (7.2), and (7.3), we must eliminate the same unknown, i.e., z. The addition of (7.2) $\times$ 2 and (7.3) is a suitable choice.

$$
\begin{array}{r}
4x + 2y + 2z = 14 \\
5x + y - 2z = 1 \\
\hline
9x + 3y = 15 \\
3x + y = 5
\end{array}
\tag{7.5}
$$

Equations (7.4) and (7.5) now form a pair of simple simultaneous equations whose difference, (7.5) − (7.4) will eliminate y.

$$3x + y = 5$$
$$\underline{x + y = 3}$$
$$2x \quad\;\; = 2$$
$$x = 1$$

From (7.4), $\qquad\qquad\qquad y = 2$

From (7.1), $\qquad\qquad\qquad z = 3$

Example 7.2. Solve the equations,

$$u + v + 1 = 0$$
$$\frac{1}{u} + \frac{1}{v} - \frac{1}{12} = 0$$

C.G.L.I. T.T. (part Qn.)

The simple addition or subtraction of these equations will not eliminate either of the unknowns u or v. The method required is to express one letter in terms of the other and substitute in the second equation.

$$u + v + 1 = 0 \tag{7.6}$$

$$\frac{1}{u} + \frac{1}{v} - \frac{1}{12} = 0 \tag{7.7}$$

From (7.6) $\qquad\qquad u = (-1 - v) \tag{7.8}$

Clearing fractions in (7.7) by multiplying each term by $12uv$,

$$12v + 12u - uv = 0 \tag{7.9}$$

Substituting from (7.8) into (7.9) for u,

$$12v + 12(-1 - v) - v(-1 - v) = 0$$
$$\therefore\; 12v - 12 - 12v + v + v^2 = 0$$
$$\therefore\; v^2 + v - 12 = 0 \tag{7.10}$$

Equation (7.10) is now recognized as a quadratic equation,

$$\therefore\; (v + 4)(v - 3) = 0$$
$$\therefore\; v = -4 \quad \text{or} \quad 3$$

From (7.8),

$$u = (-1 + 4) \quad \text{or} \quad (-1 - 3)$$
$$\therefore\; u = 3 \quad \text{or} \quad -4$$
$$\therefore\; v = -4 \quad \text{or} \quad 3$$

Example 7.3. Solve for x and y, the equations,

$$3y - 4x + 1 = 0$$
$$6x^2 + xy = 3(y^2 + 1)$$

C.G.L.I. T.T. (part Qn.)

The two equations being of different degree, i.e., the first is linear, the second quadratic, the method of substitution is required.

From $3y - 4x + 1 = 0$

$$y = \frac{4x - 1}{3} \qquad (7.11)$$

Substituting in the second equation,

$$6x^2 + \frac{x(4x - 1)}{3} = 3\left[\frac{(4x - 1)^2}{9} + 1\right]$$

Multiplying each term by 3,

$$18x^2 + 4x^2 - x = 16x^2 - 8x + 1 + 9$$
$$\therefore \; 6x^2 + 7x - 10 = 0$$
$$\therefore \; (6x - 5)(x + 2) = 0$$
$$\therefore \; x = \tfrac{5}{6} \quad \text{or} \quad -2$$

From (7.11),

$$y = \tfrac{7}{9} \quad \text{or} \quad -3$$

7.2   Equations reducible to quadratic form

The characteristic of the quadratic expression or equation is that the variable or unknown is of the second degree, with or without other terms of first degree.

Example 7.4. Solve $x^4 - 5x^2 + 6 = 0$

$$x^4 - 5x^2 + 6 = 0$$
$$\text{Let } u = x^2$$
$$\therefore \; u^2 - 5u + 6 = 0$$
$$\therefore \; (u - 3)(u - 2) = 0$$
$$\therefore \; u = 3 \quad \text{or} \quad 2$$
$$\therefore \; x^2 = 3 \quad \text{or} \quad 2$$
$$\therefore \; x = \pm\sqrt{3} \quad \text{or} \quad \pm\sqrt{2}$$

Example 7.5. Solve $x - \sqrt{x} - 6 = 0$

$$x - \sqrt{x} - 6 = 0$$

$$\text{Let } u = \sqrt{x}$$

$$\therefore u^2 - u - 6 = 0$$

$$\therefore (u - 3)(u + 2) = 0$$

$$\therefore u = 3 \quad \text{or} \quad -2$$

$$\therefore \sqrt{x} = 3 \quad \text{or} \quad -2$$

$$\therefore x = 9 \quad \text{or} \quad 4$$

In equations of this type, in which a partial solution has been squared, the final values must be tested in the original equation. It will be found that, while $x = 9$ or 4 satisfies the equation as far as the term in x is concerned, the correct values for $\sqrt{x}$ are $+3$ and -2; the alternative values of sign usually associated with square roots are not valid.

Example 7.6. Solve $e^{2x} - 2e^x - 24 = 0$.

$$e^{2x} - 2e^x - 24 = 0$$

Let $u = e^x$

$$\therefore u^2 = e^{2x}$$

$$\therefore u^2 - 2u - 24 = 0$$

$$\therefore (u - 6)(u + 4) = 0$$

$$\therefore u = 6 \quad \text{or} \quad -4$$

$$\therefore e^x = 6 \tag{7.12}$$

$$\text{or } e^x = -4 \tag{7.13}$$

The solution of equation (7.12) is obtained by use of tables of natural logarithms

$$e^x = 6$$

$$\therefore x = \log 6 \quad \text{(or } \ln 6\text{)}$$

$$\therefore x = 1 \cdot 792$$

There is no value of x for which e^x is negative. Equation (7.13), therefore, has no solution.

7.3   Theory of quadratic equations and functions

(a) The solution of the general quadratic equation, $ax^2 + bx + c = 0$, is

$$x = \frac{-b \pm \sqrt{(b^2 - 4ac)}}{2a}$$

The expression $b^2 - 4ac$ is called the 'discriminant' and its range of values leads to three separate conclusions about the solution of the equation.

(i) If $b^2 - 4ac$ is positive, the roots, i.e., the solutions of the equation, are real and different (Fig. 7.1).

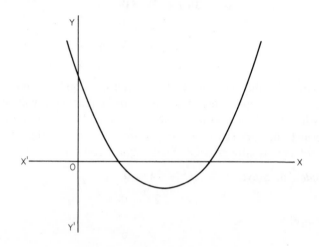

Fig. 7.1

(ii) If $b^2 - 4ac$ is zero, the roots are real and equal.
(iii) If $b^2 - 4ac$ is negative, the roots are imaginary.

Conclusions (ii) and (iii) require some illustration.

If $b^2 - 4ac$ is zero, the coincidence of the roots is not immediately obvious from the general solution,

$$x = \frac{-b \pm \sqrt{0}}{2a}, \text{ which gives only } x = -\frac{b}{2a}$$

If we consider $x^2 - 6x + 9 = 0$, in which $b^2 - 4ac = 0$, the method of factors leads to,

$$(x - 3)(x - 3) = 0$$
$$\therefore x = 3 \text{ or } 3$$

This shows the two roots to have coincided at $x = 3$. Graphically, this indicates some position of tangency to a curve, and in the above example, the x-axis is a tangent to the parabola, $y = x^2 - 6x + 9$.

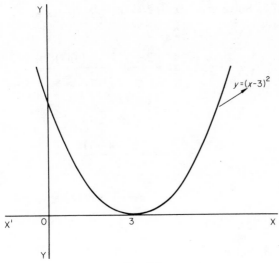

Fig. 7.2

If $b^2 - 4ac$ is negative, there is no real value of $\sqrt{(b^2 - 4ac)}$. This leads to the idea of imaginary values, depending on $\sqrt{-1}$ as a fundamental unit, to which is given the symbol 'j'. (Note, text-books in pure mathematics, not requiring to use 'i' for current, are able to represent $\sqrt{-1}$ by i.)

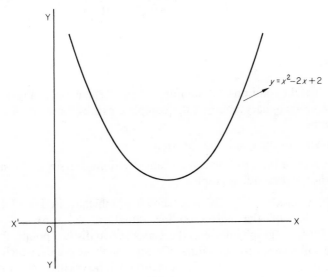

Fig. 7.3

11

Example 7.7. Solve $x^2 - 2x + 2 = 0$.

$$x^2 - 2x + 2 = 0$$

$$\therefore x = \frac{2 \pm \sqrt{\{2^2 - (4)(1)(2)\}}}{2}$$

$$= \frac{2 \pm \sqrt{-4}}{2}$$

$$= \frac{2 \pm \sqrt{4(-1)}}{2}$$

$$= \frac{2 \pm 2j}{2} \quad \text{where } j = \sqrt{-1}$$

$$= 1 \pm j$$

Example 7.8. Solve $2x^2 + 3x + 5 = 0$.

$$2x^2 + 3x + 5 = 0$$

$$\therefore x = \frac{-3 \pm \sqrt{\{9 - (4)(2)(5)\}}}{4}$$

$$= \frac{-3 \pm \sqrt{-31}}{4}$$

$$= \frac{-3 \pm \sqrt{31(-1)}}{4}$$

$$= -\frac{3}{4} \pm j \frac{\sqrt{31}}{4}$$

Each of the solutions to Examples 7.7 and 7.8 consists of a real number and an imaginary number, the complete expression being a complex number.

(b) Sign of the quadratic function

The sign of the function can be considered most easily as the sign of y in the corresponding graph.

(i) Consider $x^2 - 6x + 8$, shown graphically in Fig. 7.4. Since $b^2 - 4ac$ of the corresponding equation, $x^2 - 6x + 8 = 0$, is positive, the graph intersects the x-axis at two distinct points, P and Q, and will be negative for values of x between those points, which are the solutions of the equation. The function will be positive for values of x less than P and also for values of x greater than Q.

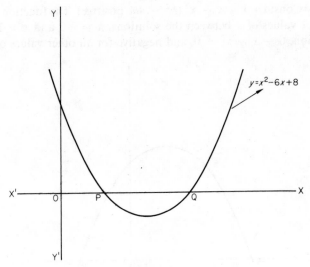

Fig. 7.4

(ii) Consider $2x^2 - 3x + 5$. Since $b^2 - 4ac$ of the corresponding equation, $2x^2 - 3x + 5 = 0$, is negative, there are no real solutions of the equation and the graph does not intersect the x-axis (Fig. 7.5).

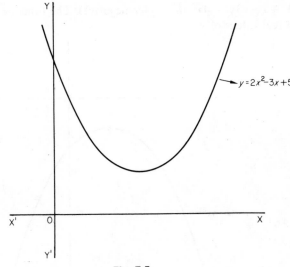

Fig. 7.5

The function, $2x^2 - 3x + 5$, is therefore positive for all real values of x.

(iii) Consider $6 - x - x^2$ ($b^2 - 4ac$ positive). The function is positive for values of x between the solutions, $x = -3$ and $x = 2$ of the equation, $6 - x - x^2 = 0$, and negative for all other values of x.

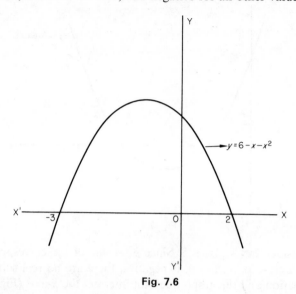

Fig. 7.6

(iv) $-2 - 3x - 4x^2$ ($b^2 - 4ac$ negative). The function is negative for all real values of x.

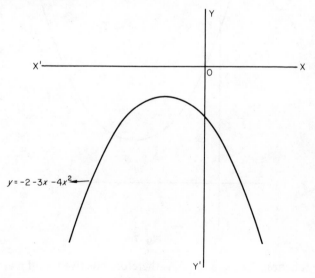

Fig. 7.7

To summarize, the quadratic expression, $ax^2 + bx + c$, has the same sign as a, except for values of x between α and β, the roots of the corresponding equation, $ax^2 + bx + c = 0$. When there is no solution to the equation, the expression has the same sign as a.

(c) Maximum and minimum values of quadratic functions

The method relies on the process of completing the square of a quadratic function and on the property of the square of an expression being positive or zero but never negative.

Example 7.9. Find, by an algebraic method, the minimum value of $x^2 - 6x + 14$, and the value of x for which the expression is a minimum.

$$x^2 - 6x + 14 = x^2 - 6x + \left(\frac{6}{2}\right)^2 + 14 - \left(\frac{6}{2}\right)^2$$

$$= (x^2 - 6x + 9) + 5$$

$$= (x - 3)^2 + 5$$

The term $(x - 3)^2$ must be positive or zero for all values of x; hence, the minimum value of $x^2 - 6x + 14$ will occur when $(x - 3)^2$ is zero, i.e., when $x = 3$, giving a minimum value for $x^2 - 6x + 14$ of $+5$.

Example 7.10. Find the maximum value of $6 - 8x - x^2$ and the value of x for which the expression is a maximum.

$$6 - 8x - x^2 = 6 - (x^2 + 8x)$$

$$= 6 - (x^2 + 8x + 16 - 16)$$

$$= 6 - (x^2 + 8x + 16) + 16$$

$$= 22 - (x + 4)^2$$

When the term $(x + 4)^2$ is zero, i.e., when $x = -4$ the expression will have a maximum value of 22.

Example 7.11. Investigate the properties of the function,
$$2x^2 - 10x + 16.$$

$$2x^2 - 10x + 16 = 2(x^2 - 5x + 8)$$

$$= 2\left[x^2 - 5x + \left(\frac{5}{2}\right)^2 + 8 - \left(\frac{5}{2}\right)^2\right]$$

$$= 2\left[\left(x - \frac{5}{2}\right)^2 + \frac{7}{4}\right]$$

Hence, the minimum value of $2x^2 - 10x + 16$ will be $\frac{7}{2}$, when $x = \frac{5}{2}$. Since the minimum value of the expression is positive, the expression will remain positive for all values of x.

(d) Sum and product of the roots of a quadratic equation

Let the solution of the general quadratic equation $ax^2 + bx + c = 0$, be α and β.

Let

$$\alpha = \frac{-b + \sqrt{(b^2 - 4ac)}}{2a} \quad \text{and} \quad \beta = \frac{-b - \sqrt{(b^2 - 4ac)}}{2a}$$

$$\therefore \; \alpha + \beta = \frac{-b + \sqrt{(b^2 - 4ac)} - b - \sqrt{(b^2 - 4ac)}}{2a}$$

$$= -\frac{2b}{2a} = -\frac{b}{a}$$

That is, sum of roots $= -b/a$.

Similarly

$$\alpha\beta = \frac{\left[-b + \sqrt{(b^2 - 4ac)}\right]}{2a} \times \frac{\left[-b - \sqrt{(b^2 - 4ac)}\right]}{2a}$$

$$= \frac{\left[\sqrt{(b^2 - 4ac)} - b\right]}{2a} \times \frac{-\left[\sqrt{(b^2 - 4ac)} + b\right]}{2a}$$

(The factors of the numerator are now in the form of the difference of two squares)

$$= \frac{-(b^2 - 4ac - b^2)}{4a^2}$$

$$= \frac{-(-4ac)}{4a^2} = \frac{c}{a}$$

That is, product of roots $= c/a$.

(e) Formation of the quadratic equation whose roots are given

Consider the method of solution by factors of $x^2 - 5x + 6 = 0$

$$x^2 - 5x + 6 = 0 \tag{7.14}$$

$$\therefore \; (x - 3)(x - 2) = 0 \tag{7.15}$$

$$\therefore \; x = 3 \text{ or } 2 \tag{7.16}$$

To form the equation from the given roots, we now read the stages in the order (7.16), (7.15), (7.14). If, however, the given equation had been $2(x^2 - 5x + 6) = 0$, the solutions would still be 3 or 2. Hence we make allowance for the possibility of a multiplying constant.

In general, if α and β are the roots of a quadratic equation, then the equation can be written as,

$$a(x - \alpha)(x - \beta) = 0$$
$$\therefore a[x^2 - (\alpha + \beta)x + \alpha\beta] = 0$$
$$a[x^2 - (\text{sum of roots})x + \text{product of roots}] = 0$$

Example 7.12. Write down the sum and product of the roots of the equation $2x^2 - x - 10 = 0$ and check the answer by finding the roots.

$$\text{Sum} = -\frac{b}{a} = -\frac{(-1)}{2} = \frac{1}{2}$$

$$\text{Product} = \frac{c}{a} = \frac{-10}{2} = -5$$

Check:

$$2x^2 - x - 10 = 0$$
$$\therefore (2x - 5)(x + 2) = 0$$
$$\therefore x = 2\tfrac{1}{2} \text{ or } -2$$

Hence the sum $= \frac{1}{2}$ and the product $= -5$.

Example 7.13. If α and β are the roots of $2x^2 - 5x - 1 = 0$ find the value of $(2\alpha + \beta)(\alpha + 2\beta)$.

$$\begin{aligned}
(2\alpha + \beta)(\alpha + 2\beta) &= 2\alpha^2 + 5\alpha\beta + 2\beta^2 \\
&= 2\alpha^2 + 4\alpha\beta + 2\beta^2 + \alpha\beta \\
&= 2(\alpha + \beta)^2 + \alpha\beta \\
&= 2(\text{sum of roots})^2 + \text{product of roots} \\
&= 2\left(\frac{5}{2}\right)^2 - \frac{1}{2} \\
&= 12
\end{aligned}$$

Example 7.14. If α and β are the roots of the equation,
$$4x^2 + 3x - 2 = 0$$
find the equation whose roots are $1/\alpha$ and $1/\beta$.

The required equation is,

$$a\left(x - \frac{1}{\alpha}\right)\left(x - \frac{1}{\beta}\right) = 0$$

$$\therefore a\left[x^2 - x\left(\frac{1}{\alpha} + \frac{1}{\beta}\right) + \frac{1}{\alpha\beta}\right] = 0$$

$$\therefore a\left[x^2 - x\left(\frac{\beta + \alpha}{\alpha\beta}\right) + \frac{1}{\alpha\beta}\right] = 0$$

From the given equation, $4x^2 + 3x - 2 = 0$, $\alpha + \beta = -\frac{3}{4}$, and $\alpha\beta = -\frac{1}{2}$. Hence the required equation is,

$$a\left[x^2 - x\left(\frac{-\frac{3}{4}}{-\frac{1}{2}}\right) + \frac{1}{(-\frac{1}{2})}\right] = 0$$

$$\therefore a\left[x^2 - \frac{3x}{2} - 2\right] = 0$$

7.4 Transposition of formulae involving the constant 'e'

The constant 'e' occurs in formulae in two closely connected forms, (a) as the base of natural logarithms, and (b) as the base of an exponential term, e.g., e^x. It is useful to recall the definition of a logarithm to show this connection.

$$\text{If } \log N = x$$

$$\text{then } N = e^x$$

Example 7.15. If $i = (V/R)(1 - e^{-Rt/L})$, find an expression for t.

$$i = \frac{V}{R}\left(1 - e^{-Rt/L}\right)$$

$$\therefore \frac{Ri}{V} = 1 - e^{-Rt/L}$$

$$\therefore e^{-Rt/L} = 1 - \frac{Ri}{V} = \frac{V - Ri}{V}$$

$$-\frac{Rt}{L} = \log\left(\frac{V - Ri}{V}\right)$$

$$\therefore t = -\frac{L}{R}\log\left(\frac{V - Ri}{V}\right)$$

Example 7.16. If $t = CR \log [V/(V - v)]$, find an expression for v.

$$t = CR \log \left(\frac{V}{V - v}\right)$$

$$\therefore \frac{t}{CR} = \log \left(\frac{V}{V - v}\right)$$

$$\therefore e^{t/CR} = \frac{V}{V - v}$$

$$\therefore e^{t/CR}(V - v) = V$$

$$\therefore e^{t/CR}V - e^{t/CR}v = V$$

$$\therefore e^{t/CR}V - V = e^{t/CR}v$$

Divide both sides of the equation by $e^{t/CR}$,

$$\therefore V - Ve^{-t/CR} = v$$

$$\therefore V(1 - e^{-t/CR}) = v$$

7.5   Logarithmic equations

Example 7.17. Solve $2 \log a = \log 2 + \log (3a - 4)$.

$$2 \log a = \log 2 + \log (3a - 4)$$

$$\therefore \log (a^2) = \log [2(3a - 4)]$$

$$\therefore a^2 = 2(3a - 4)$$

$$\therefore a^2 - 6a + 8 = 0$$

$$\therefore (a - 2)(a - 4) = 0$$

$$\therefore a = 2 \text{ or } 4$$

Example 7.18. Solve $2 \cdot 7^x = 16 \cdot 8$.

Taking logarithms of both sides, to base 10,

$$x \log_{10} 2 \cdot 7 = \log_{10} 16 \cdot 8$$

$$\therefore x = \frac{\log_{10} 16 \cdot 8}{\log_{10} 2 \cdot 7}$$

No.	log
1·225	0·0882
0·4314	$\bar{1}$·6349
2·840	0·4533

$$= \frac{1 \cdot 2253}{0 \cdot 4314}$$

$$= 2 \cdot 840$$

Example 7.19. Solve $x^{1.56} = 43.7$

Taking logarithms of both sides, to base 10,

$$1.56 \log_{10} x = \log_{10} 43.7$$

$$\therefore \log_{10} x = \frac{\log_{10} 43.7}{1.56}$$

No.	log
1.641	0.2151
1.56	0.1931
1.052	0.0220

$$= \frac{1.6405}{1.56}$$

$$= 1.052$$

$$\therefore x = 11.27$$

EXERCISE 7.1

1. In a certain network, the currents I_1, I_2, I_3 are related by the following equations;

$$3I_1 + 2I_2 + 6I_3 = 27.5$$
$$3I_1 + 4(I_2 - I_3) = 2.5$$
$$6(I_3 - I_1) + 4I_2 = 19$$

Solve these equations to find the values of $I_1, I_2,$ and I_3.

2. In the given figure, calculate the values of the currents $I_1, I_2,$ and I_3.

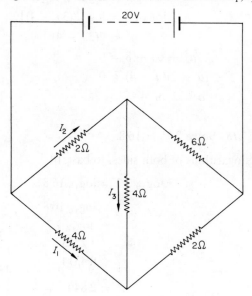

Fig. 7.8

3. Solve the equations,

$$x + y - z = 1$$
$$2x - y + 2z = 9 \cdot 5$$
$$3x + 2y - 2z = 4$$

4. In a certain electrical network, currents x, y, and z are given by the simultaneous equations,

$$5x - 3y = 10$$
$$3x - 8y + 3z = 0$$
$$3y - 7z = 5$$

Calculate the value of y.

U.L.C.I. (part Qn.)

5. Solve the equations,

$$y + 4x = 6$$
$$2x^2 + xy + y^2 = 8$$

6. Solve $x^4 + 4x^2 - 32 = 0$.

7. Solve $2x - 5x^{1/2} - 3 = 0$.

8. Solve $6e^x + 5 - 6/e^x = 0$.

9. Investigate the sign of the function $2x^2 - 14x + 20$.

10. Write down the sum and the product of the roots of each of the following equations.
    (a) $3x^2 - 5x + 2 = 0$ (b) $3x - 2/x = 1$
    (c) $2bx^2 - ax + 3c = 0$ (d) $x = 1/x$

11. If the roots of the equation $4x^2 + Ax + 2 = 0$ are equal, find the value of A.

12. If α and β are the roots of the equation $2x^2 - 5x - 8 = 0$, write down the values of;
    (a) $\alpha + \beta$ (b) $\alpha\beta$
    (c) $\alpha^2 + \beta^2$ (d) $(\alpha - \beta)^2$

13. Find, by an algebraic method, the maximum or minimum values of the following functions and the values of x for which they occur.
    (a) $x^2 - 8x + 4$ (b) $2x^2 + 7x + 10$
    (c) $4 - 3x - x^2$ (d) $6 - 4x - 3x^2$

14. The heating time of a coil through which an electric current flows is given by,

$$\theta = \theta_m(1 - e^{-t/T})$$

Transpose the formula to make t the subject.

15. When a capacitor is discharged through a non-inductive resistor, the p.d. across the plates is given by,

$$v = V_0 e^{-t/CR}$$

Find an expression for C.

16. The capacity of a concentric cable is given by,

$$C = \frac{k}{\log (R/r)^2}$$

Make r the subject of the formula.

17. Given $\tan \psi = \dfrac{V}{2 \cdot 5x \log (D/d)}$, find an expression for D.

18. The charge on a capacitor is given by,

$$q = CV(1 - e^{-t/CR})$$

Transpose the formula to make t the subject.

19. Solve $\log_{10} 6 - 2 \log_{10} x = 1 \cdot 4$.

20. Solve $\log_{10} (2 \cdot 7 + x) + 2 = \log_{10} 1500$.

21. Solve $\log_{10} (15 \cdot 2/x) - \log 35 \cdot 7 = \log_{10} 3 \cdot 8$.

22. Solve $(2x)^{1 \cdot 38} = 210 \cdot 7$.

23. Solve $(0 \cdot 75)^{x+1} = 1 \cdot 6(10^{-3})$

24. Solve $e^{-x^2} = 0 \cdot 1353$.

25. If $2 \log p - \log N = \log t - 2$ and the logarithms are to the base 10, give, in its simplest form, an expression for p in terms of N and t.

C.G.L.I. E.T. (part Qn.)

26. (a) Solve for x and y the equations

$$3y - 4x + 1 = 0$$
$$6x^2 + xy = 3(y^2 + 1)$$

(b) By rearranging the function $y = 3x^2 - 14x + 18$ in the form $y = a(x + b)^2 + c$ where a, b, and c are constants, show that y cannot be less than $1\frac{2}{3}$. What is the value of x and of dy/dx, when $y = 1\frac{2}{3}$?

C.G.L.I. T.T.

27. (a) If $\log_{10}(10 + 9x) - \log_{10}(11 - x) = 2$, find x.

(b) Prove that $(\log_2 N)/(\log_3 N)$ is independent of the number N, and calculate its value to three significant figures.

[Hint, not given in examination; let $\log_2 N = x$ and let $\log_3 N = y$.]

(c) A system of n receivers is said to have a diversity gain of G decibels given by,

$$G = \frac{20}{m}\left(1 - \frac{1}{n}\right)\log_e\left(\frac{1}{k}\right)$$

where k is the proportion of time loss allowed, and m is a constant for the system.

(i) If $m = 2\cdot1$ when $n = 3$ and $k = 0\cdot2$, calculate G.

(ii) Express k in terms of G, m, and n.

C.G.L.I. T.T.

28. In a network, the mesh currents i_1, i_2, i_3 amperes are related by the equations

$$10i_2 + 25(i_2 + i_3) = 2$$
$$9i_1 + 10i_3 - 10i_2 = 0$$
$$9i_1 + 24(i_1 - i_3) = 2$$

Calculate the current i_1 to the nearest mA.

C.G.L.I. T.T. (part Qn.)

29. (a) Write down the conditions that the roots of the quadratic equation $ax^2 + bx + c = 0$, may be real and of the same sign.

(b) Show that if one root of the equation,

$$px^2 + qx + r = 0$$

is three times the other, then $3q^2 = 16pr$.

U.L.C.I. O2.

30. (a) Sketch the curve whose equation is $y = ax^2 + bx + c$ such that its minimum value is -8, and y is negative only when $1 < x < 5$. Find the values of the constants a, b, and c.

(b) Show that for the equation $4(x - 2)^2 = p(x - 1)$ the sum of the roots equals their product for all values of p. If the roots differ by $3\frac{3}{4}$, find the possible values of p.

C.G.L.I. T.T.

31. (a) The difference between two numbers is 10 and the difference between their squares is also 10. Find the numbers.

(b) Solve the simultaneous equations,

$$\frac{1}{x} + \frac{1}{y} = \frac{1}{2} \quad \text{and} \quad 2x - y = 9$$

N.C.T.E.C.

32. (a) An unknown resistance is placed in parallel with a resistance of 6 ohms. It is now placed in series with the 6 ohms resistance and it is found that the combined resistance has increased to four and a half times what it was before. Find the value of the unknown resistance.

(b) Solve the simultaneous equations;

$$x^2 + y^2 = 40$$
$$x + 2y = 2$$

E.M.E.U.

33. Solve the simultaneous equations;

$$x + 3y - 2z = 9$$
$$3x - 6y + 2z = 1$$
$$x + 6y - 3z = 13$$

C.G.L.I. T.T. (part Qn.)

34. The formula $M = k \log_e \left[(d^2 + 4h^2)/d^2 \right]$ describes the mutual inductance M of an open-wire pair at a height h above the ground.

    Change the subject of this formula to give h in terms of M, k, and d.

C.G.L.I. T.T. (part Qn.)

35. Solve the simultaneous equations;

$$3y - 2x = 12$$
$$\frac{1}{x} + \frac{1}{y} = \frac{1}{6}$$

N.C.T.E.C. (part Qn.)

36. Solve the equations;

$$a - b + c = 0$$
$$2a + b - 3c = 0$$
$$a^2 + 2b^2 + 3c^2 = 9$$

C.G.L.I. T.T. (part Qn.)

8. Graphs

8.1 Sketch graphs

A graph is the pictorial representation of the dependence of one variable on another, and it is often sufficient to be able to sketch the graph rather than to plot it accurately. For this purpose, we must recognize certain characteristics in the graphical function.

The degree of the function

In general, this may be considered as the highest power of the variables.

(a) Linear, $y = mx + c$.

(b) Quadratic, $y = f(x^2)$, giving a parabola.

(c) Reciprocal, $y = 1/f(x)$, giving a hyperbola.

(d) $x^2 + y^2 = r^2$, giving a circle.

(a) The straight-line graph has been discussed fully in Volumes 1 and 2.

(b) Parabola, $y = f(x^2)$

Is x a factor of $f(x)^2$?

Consider $y = x^2$, $y = x^2 - 4x$, $y = 6x - x^2$. In each of these examples, the graph is a parabola which passes through the origin, i.e., when $x = 0$, $y = 0$.

For what value of x is $y = 0$?

Consider
$$y = x^2 - 5x + 6$$

Let $y = 0$, then

$$0 = x^2 - 5x + 6$$
$$\therefore\ 0 = (x - 3)(x - 2)$$
$$\therefore\ x = 3 \text{ or } 2$$

The x-axis is the line $y = 0$, hence the graph intersects the x-axis at $x = 3$ and $x = 2$.

If $x = 0$, what is the value of y?

Consider $\qquad\qquad y = x^2 - 5x + 6$

If $x = 0$, $y = 6$.

The y-axis is the line $x = 0$, hence the graph intersects the y-axis at $y = 6$.

Is $f(x^2)$ a perfect square, i.e., $b^2 - 4ac = 0$?

Consider $\qquad\qquad\qquad y = x^2 - 6x + 9$
$$\therefore\ y = (x - 3)^2$$

Hence y is positive or zero for all values of x.

Let $y = 0$, then

$$(x - 3)^2 = 0$$
$$\therefore\ x = 3 \text{ or } 3$$

The graph is tangential to the x-axis at $x = 3$.

Turning points

Consider $\qquad\qquad\qquad y = 2x^2 - 6x + 3$

$$\therefore\ \frac{dy}{dx} = 4x - 6$$

$$\therefore\ \frac{d^2y}{dx^2} = 4$$

The graph has a minimum turning point when $4x - 6 = 0$, i.e., $x = 1\frac{1}{2}$.

(c) Reciprocal, $y = 1/f(x)$, giving a hyperbola.

Example 8.1. Consider $y = k/x$. This represents inverse variation, in which one variable increases as the other decreases, and vice versa. As x becomes very small, y becomes very large, and at $x = 0$, $y = \infty$. At this point, we are unable to plot the graph, and this is indicated by the use of a line called an 'asymptote', shown as a broken line in Fig. 8.1.

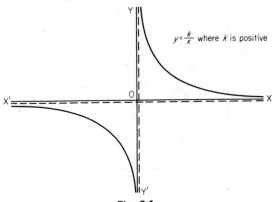

Fig. 8.1

Example 8.2. Consider

$$y = \frac{9}{2x - 4}$$

The function is still in reciprocal form, the constants now included altering only the general scale and position of the hyperbola. The value of y will be infinitely large when $2x - 4 = 0$, i.e., $x = 2$.

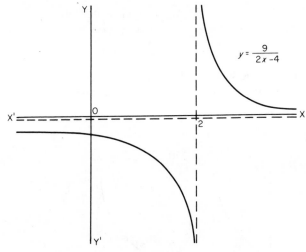

Fig. 8.2

It will be noted in Examples 8.1 and 8.2, that when $y = 0$, $x = \infty$ giving a second asymptote along the x-axis.

Example 8.3. The growth of current in an inductive circuit provides a good example of an asymptote.

12

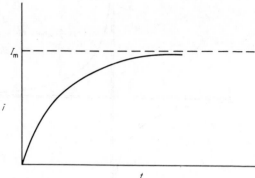

Fig. 8.3

$$i = I_m(1 - e^{-Rt/L})$$

where R and L are constants.

As t increases, $e^{-Rt/L}$ decreases, hence $(1 - e^{-Rt/L})$ increases. When t is very large, theoretically approaching infinity, $e^{-Rt/L}$ is practically zero and the current approaches its final steady value I_m; the time at which this occurs is governed by the ratio R/L.

If $t = L/R$, then

$$e^{-Rt/L} = e^{-1} = 0.3679$$
$$\therefore\ i = I_m(1 - 0.3679)$$
$$= 0.6321 I_m$$
$$= 63.2\% \, I_m$$

The time $t = L/R$, in which the current rises to 63.2% of its final steady value, is the characteristic of the inductor known as the time constant.

Example 8.4. $y = \tan\theta$

when $\theta = 90°$ $y = \pm\infty$

when $\theta = 270°$ $y = \pm\infty$

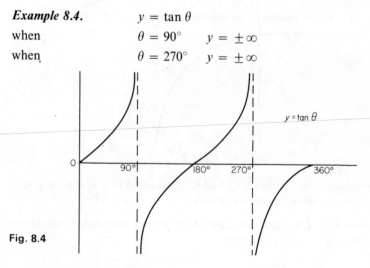

Fig. 8.4

(d) Circle, centre the origin, radius r, $x^2 + y^2 = r^2$

This graph provides a simple opportunity of deriving the equation by first principles from the geometrical definition.

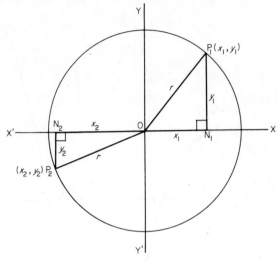

Fig. 8.5

All points on the circumference are at a constant distance from the centre. Let P_1 (x_1, y_1) and P_2 (x_2, y_2) be any two points on the circumference. Draw P_1N_1 and P_2N_2 perpendicular to the x-axis. By the theorem of Pythagoras in triangles OP_1N_1 and OP_2N_2,

$$x_1{}^2 + y_1{}^2 = r^2$$

and

$$x_2{}^2 + y_2{}^2 = r^2$$

Since this will be true for all positions of the point P, the equation of the circle is,

$$x^2 + y^2 = r^2$$

Graphs of the form $e^{\pm pt} \sin \omega t$, where p and ω are constants

Example 8.5. Plot the graph of $y = e^{2t} \sin 5t$.

t (sec):	0	0·1	0·2	0·3	0·4	0·5	0·6
$5t$ (rad):	0	0·5	1·0	1·5	2·0	2·5	3·0
$\sin 5t$:	0	0·48	0·84	1·0	0·91	0·60	0·14
e^{2t}:	1	1·22	1·49	1·82	2·23	2·72	3·30
$y = e^{2t} \sin 5t$:	0	0·59	1·3	1·8	2·0	1·6	0·46

t (sec):	0·7	0·8	0·9	1·0	1·1	1·2	1·3	1·4
$5t$ (rad):	3·5	4·0	4·5	5·0	5·5	6·0	6·5	7·0
$\sin 5t$:	−0·35	−0·76	−0·98	−0·96	−0·71	−0·28	0·22	0·66
e^{2t}:	4·05	4·95	6·05	7·39	9·03	11·0	13·5	16·5
$y = e^{2t} \sin 5t$:	−1·4	−3·8	−5·9	−7·1	−6·4	−3·1	3·0	11·0

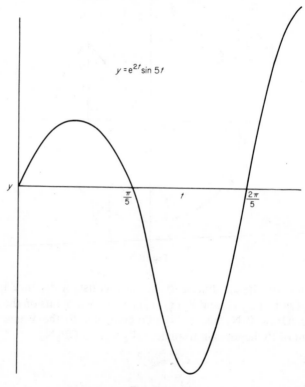

Fig. 8.6

We observe that the factor e^{pt} applied to the wave form of $\sin \omega t$ has introduced an element of instability. The maximum value of $\sin 5t$ is $+1$ and the minimum value is -1. In the graph of $y = e^{2t} \sin 5t$, the maximum value is $+2$ and the minimum value is -7, within the range of values plotted, but it can be shown that the magnitudes of successive turning-points become progressively larger.

Example 8.6. Plot the graph of $y = e^{-2t} \sin 5t$.

The table of values is largely the same as in Example 8.5 apart from the negative power of 'e'.

The factor e^{-pt} is said to have a 'damping effect' on the wave form of $\sin \omega t$; the magnitude of successive turning-points becoming progres-

sively smaller. It is interesting to note that the curves $y = e^{-2t}$ and
$y = -e^{-2t}$ are boundaries to the given curve; in this position, they are
said to be the 'envelopes' of $y = e^{-2t} \sin 5t$.

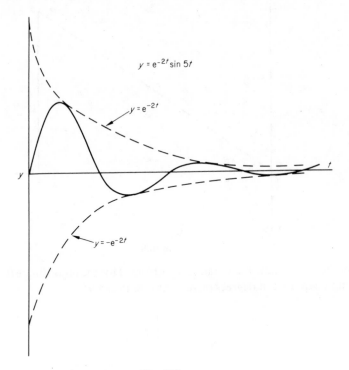

Fig. 8.7

8.2 Polar co-ordinates

In plotting graphs, we have identified the positions of points by
measurements from two axes at right-angles; such measurements are
known as 'rectangular or cartesian' co-ordinates.

In Fig. 8.8, to reach the point P starting from O, we could imagine our
instructions to be ,'walk x metres due East to Q, turn North and walk y
metres to P'. It would be more concise to say 'walk r metres in a direction $\theta°$ North of East'. These two measurements, a direct length from
O and an angular measurement from OX, are given the name 'polar
co-ordinates'. The point O is known as the 'pole' and OX as 'the
initial line'; the y-axis is not required. Graph paper for this purpose is
graduated in concentric circles with O as centre, giving measurements

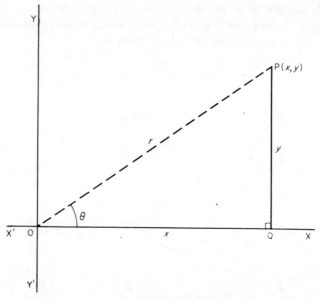

Fig. 8.8

of the co-ordinate r, and radial lines from O for the co-ordinate θ, which can be quoted in degrees or radians (see Fig. 8.9)

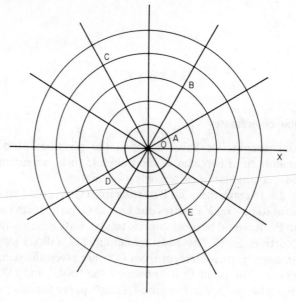

Fig. 8.9

A has co-ordinates (1, 30°)
B   ,,   ,,   (3, 60°)
C   ,,   ,,   (4, 120°)
D   ,,   ,,   (a) (2, 210°) or (b) (−2, 30°)
E   ,,   ,,   (a) (3, 300°) or (b) (−3, 120°) or
                         (c) (3, −60°)

Signs of the co-ordinates

Angles are positive when measured in an anticlockwise direction from
OX, following the usual convention. When this direction has been
fixed, a positive value of the co-ordinate r is measured outwards from O
along that radius vector, as in OA, OB, OC, OD(a) and OE(a) and (c).

In D(b) and E(b), having fixed the directions 30° and 120°, we must
measure 2 and 3 units respectively backwards, to reach D and E.

In E(c), having fixed the direction −60°, we measure outwards along
this line from O to make $r = +3$.

Polar graph paper is graduated at much more frequent intervals than
it is possible to show in Fig. 8.9.

Conversion of cartesian co-ordinates to polar co-ordinates

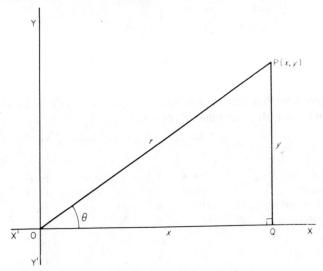

Fig. 8.10

Let the point P have co-ordinates (x, y) and in polar form (r, θ), using
OX as the initial line.

From $\triangle OPQ$,

$$x = r \cos \theta \quad \text{and} \quad y = r \sin \theta$$

or conversely,

$$r = \sqrt{(x^2 + y^2)} \quad \text{and} \quad \tan \theta = y/x$$

Example 8.7. Find the polar equation of the curve $y = 4x^2$.

Substituting $y = r \sin \theta$ and $x = r \cos \theta$

$$r \sin \theta = 4r^2 \cos^2 \theta$$

$$\sin \theta = 4r \cos^2 \theta$$

$$r = \frac{\sin \theta}{4 \cos^2 \theta}$$

Example 8.8. Find the cartesian equation of the curve,

$$r = \frac{2 \cos \theta}{\cos \theta - \sin \theta}$$

$$r = \frac{\dfrac{2 \cos \theta}{\cos \theta}}{\dfrac{\cos \theta}{\cos \theta} - \dfrac{\sin \theta}{\cos \theta}} = \frac{2}{1 - \tan \theta}$$

$$\therefore \ \sqrt{(x^2 + y^2)} = \frac{2}{1 - y/x} = \frac{2x}{x - y}$$

$$\therefore \ x^2 + y^2 = \frac{4x^2}{(x - y)^2}$$

Example 8.9. Plot the curve given by $r = 6(1 + \cos \theta)$ for values of θ from 0 to 2π radians at intervals of $\pi/6$.

θ	0	$\dfrac{\pi}{6}$	$\dfrac{\pi}{3}$	$\dfrac{\pi}{2}$	$\dfrac{2\pi}{3}$	$\dfrac{5\pi}{6}$
$\cos \theta$:	1	0·866	0·5	0	−0·5	−0·866
$1 + \cos \theta$:	2	1·866	1·5	1	0·5	0·134
$r = 6(1 + \cos \theta)$:	12	11·2	9	6	3	0·8
Points on curve:	P	Q	R	S	T	U

θ	π	$\dfrac{7\pi}{6}$	$\dfrac{4\pi}{3}$	$\dfrac{3\pi}{2}$	$\dfrac{5\pi}{3}$	$\dfrac{11\pi}{6}$	2π
$\cos \theta$:	−1	−0·866	−0·5	0	0·5	0·866	1
$1 + \cos \theta$:	0	0·134	0·5	1	1·5	1·866	2
$r = 6(1 + \cos \theta)$:	0	0·8	3	6	9	11·2	12
Points on curve:	O	V	W	L	M	N	P

Since polar co-ordinates involve magnitude and direction, they are readily recognized as vectors and have important applications in measuring the strength of radiation of heat, light, sound, or radio signals in different directions from the source. In Fig. 8.11, a transmitter

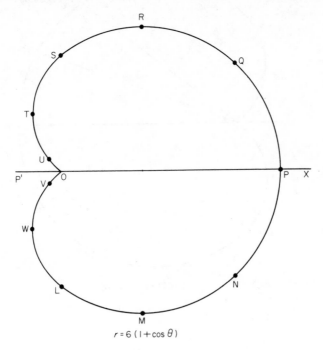

$r = 6 \, (1 + \cos \theta)$

Fig. 8.11

at O would produce a maximum signal strength in the direction OP and a minimum in the opposite direction OP'; between OU and OV, the signal strength could possibly be regarded as negligible.

Area enclosed by a curve expressed in polar form

Let the point B (Fig. 8.12) have co-ordinates (r, θ) and let the point C have co-ordinates $(r + \delta r, \theta + \delta \theta)$. The element of area enclosed by OB, OC, and the arc BC is then a sector of the total area, and if the points B and C are close together, i.e., $\delta \theta$ is very small, then the sector can be regarded as a sector of a circle, radius r.

Hence

$$\delta(\text{area}) = \tfrac{1}{2} r^2 (\delta \theta)$$

where $\delta \theta$ is in radians.

The total area enclosed by the whole curve can now be found by the summation of all such sectors using the process of integral calculus.

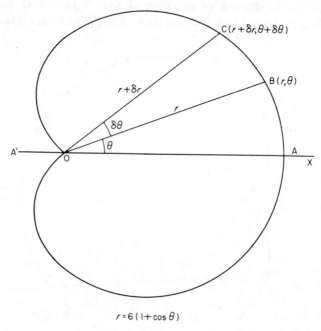

$$r = 6(1 + \cos\theta)$$

Fig. 8.12

The limits of integration will be from $\theta = 0$, representing OA, to $\theta = \pi$, representing OA', the result to be doubled to include the symmetrical lower half of the area.

$$
\begin{aligned}
\text{Total area} &= 2\int_0^\pi \frac{1}{2} r^2 \, d\theta \\
&= \int_0^\pi 36(1 + \cos\theta)^2 \, d\theta \\
&= 36\int_0^\pi (1 + 2\cos\theta + \cos^2\theta) \, d\theta \\
&= 36\int_0^\pi \left[1 + 2\cos\theta + \frac{1}{2}(1 + \cos 2\theta)\right] d\theta \\
&= 36\int_0^\pi \left(\frac{3}{2} + 2\cos\theta + \frac{1}{2}\cos 2\theta\right) d\theta
\end{aligned}
$$

$$= 36 \left[\frac{3\theta}{2} + 2 \sin \theta + \frac{1}{2} \frac{\sin 2\theta}{2} \right]_0^\pi$$

$$= 36 \left[\frac{3\pi}{2} + 0 \right] - 36[0]$$

$$= 54\pi \text{ square units}$$

A comparison can be made at this point with the mean value of an alternating current, which also utilizes the area under a curve. The mean value of the radius r of the given curve is the radius of a circle of equal area. Hence,

$$\pi(r_{\text{mean}})^2 = 54\pi$$

$$\therefore \quad r_{\text{mean}} = \sqrt{54} = 7{\cdot}35$$

EXERCISE 8.1

1. Sketch, not plot, the following graphs, indicating any significant values and showing asymptotes by broken lines.

   (a) $y - 3x + 2 = 0$ (b) $\dfrac{x}{5} + \dfrac{y}{8} = 1$

   (c) $\dfrac{y}{x} = 1$ (d) $y = x^2$

   (e) $y = 4x - x^2$ (f) $y = x^2 - 8x + 16$

   (g) $y = 3x^2 - 2x + 5$ (h) $y = 4x^2 + 4x - 3$

   (i) $y = 6 - 5x - 6x^2$ (j) $x^2 + y^2 = 25$

   (k) $4x^2 + 4y^2 = 49$

2. Sketch the following graphs

   (a) $y = \dfrac{1}{x - 2}$ (b) $3y + 2xy - 4 = 0$

   (c) $y = 4 \tan\left(2\theta - \dfrac{\pi}{4}\right)$ (d) $\theta = \theta_\text{m}(1 - e^{-t/T})$

   (e) $q = Q(1 - e^{-t/CR})$ (f) $y = \dfrac{6}{2x - 5}$

   (g) $y = 2 \tan\left(\theta + \dfrac{\pi}{4}\right)$ (h) $v = V_0\, e^{-t/CR}$

   (i) $i = I\, e^{-Rt/L}$ (j) $y = 1 - e^{-x}$

3. Indicate on a sketch the positions of points whose polar co-ordinates are given below; show the meaning of the co-ordinates for each point.

(a) A, $(1, 30°)$

(b) B, $\left(2, \dfrac{\pi}{3}\right)$

(c) C, $\left(-2, \dfrac{\pi}{4}\right)$

(d) D, $(3, 150°)$

(e) E, $(2, -30°)$

(f) F, $\left(1, -\dfrac{2\pi}{3}\right)$

(g) G, $(-1, -\pi)$

4. Assuming the origin O of cartesian co-ordinates is the same point as O, the pole of polar co-ordinates, and the x-axis is the initial line, find the x and y co-ordinates of the following points given in polar co-ordinates.

(a) $(2, \pi/3)$

(b) $(5, 2\pi/3)$

(c) $(-3, \pi/2)$

(d) $(4, 210°)$

(e) $(6, -30°)$

(f) $(-2, \pi/6)$

(g) $(-8, -5\pi/6)$

(h) $(12, 0)$

(i) $(-1, 11\pi/6)$

(j) $(3, -\pi/2)$

5. Assuming the conditions of question 4, find the polar co-ordinates of the following points whose cartesian co-ordinates are given; quote θ in the form $\tan^{-1}(a/b)$.

(a) $(3, 4)$

(b) $(5, 12)$

(c) $(-2, 5)$

(d) $(-6, 3)$

(e) $(-1, -1)$

(f) $(7, -24)$

(g) $(10, -10)$

(h) $(-4, -4)$

(i) $(\sqrt{2}, \sqrt{3})$

(j) $(-\sqrt{5}, -\sqrt{8})$

6. Find the polar equations of the curves given below in cartesian form.

(a) $y = 4x^2$

(b) $y = 6x - x^2$

(c) $x^2 + y^2 = 16$

(d) $(x - 3)^2 + y^2 = 9$

(e) $y = 4/x$

(f) $y - 8x + 2 = 0$

(g) $\dfrac{x^2}{9} + \dfrac{y^2}{16} = 1$

(h) $y(x + 2) = 10$

(i) $x = 4y^2$

(j) $y^2 = x^2(x^2 - 4)$

7. Find the cartesian equations of the curves given below in polar
   form.
   (a) $r = 2 \sin \theta$ (b) $r \sin \theta = 2$
   (c) $r = 4$ (d) $\theta = \pi/3$
   (e) $r = 6(1 + \cos \theta)$ (f) $r = 12 \sin 2\theta$
   (g) $r^2 = 4 \cos 2\theta$

8. Calculate the area bounded by the curve $r = 3 \sin \theta$ and the lines
   $\theta = 0$ and $\theta = \pi$.

9. Draw the graph of $r = 4 \cos 2\theta$ for values of θ from 0 to 2π at
   intervals of $\pi/6$.

10. Sketch the graph of the polar curve, $4/r = 1 - \cos \theta$ as θ varies
    from $-\pi$ to $+\pi$. How would you describe the shape of this graph?
    Show that with the same origin and with the initial line as x-axis,
    the cartesian equation of this curve is $y^2 = 8(x + 2)$.
    C.G.L.I. T.T.

11. Plot the function $y = e^{-x} \sin 2x$ where x is in radians, from $x = 0$
    to $x = \pi/2$ at intervals of $\pi/8$.
        Use Simpson's rule to evaluate the approximate area between
    the x-axis and the curve, and hence deduce the mean value of
    $e^{-x} \sin 2x$ from $x = 0$ to $x = \pi/2$.
    C.G.L.I. T.T.

12. Sketch the graph of the curve whose equation in polar co-ordinates
    is $r^2 = a^2 \cos 2\theta$ for values of θ from 0 to π radians. For what
    range(s) of values of θ is there no curve?
    C.G.L.I. T.T. (part Qn.)

13. (a) A circle is drawn on OA as diameter, where OA $= 2a$. Prove
    that its equation is $r = 2a \cos \theta$ in polar co-ordinates, with O as
    pole and OA as initial line. Convert this equation to rectangular
    co-ordinates, with O as origin and OA as x-axis.

    (b) A cam profile is of the form $r = a(3 + 2 \cos \theta)$ in polar co-
    ordinates. Sketch the graph of this profile, from $\theta = 0$ to
    $\theta = 2\pi$.
    C.G.L.I. T.T.

9. Trigonometry and Calculus

9.1 Small angles; approximations

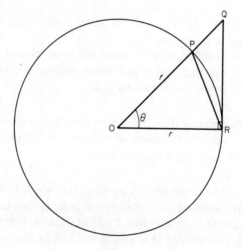

Fig. 9.1

In Fig. 9.1, QR is a tangent to the circle at R; let angle θ be an acute angle.

In $\triangle OQR$,

$$QR = r \tan \theta$$
$$\therefore \text{ Area } \triangle OQR = \tfrac{1}{2}r^2 \tan \theta$$

Area of sector OPR $= \tfrac{1}{2}r^2\theta$, where θ is in radians

Area of $\triangle OPR = \frac{1}{2}r^2 \sin \theta$

Area $\triangle OPR <$ area of sector OPR $<$ area $\triangle OQR$

$$\therefore \ \tfrac{1}{2}r^2 \sin \theta < \tfrac{1}{2}r^2\theta < \tfrac{1}{2}r^2 \tan \theta$$

$$\therefore \ \sin \theta < \theta < \tan \theta$$

Since $\sin \theta$ is positive, it is valid to divide this inequality by it.

$$\therefore \ 1 < \frac{\theta}{\sin \theta} < \frac{\tan \theta}{\sin \theta}$$

$$\therefore \ 1 < \frac{\theta}{\sin \theta} < \frac{1}{\cos \theta}$$

Thus the value of $\theta/\sin \theta$ lies between 1 and $1/\cos \theta$. As θ decreases and approaches zero, then $1/\cos \theta \to 1$; hence the value of $\theta/\sin \theta \to 1$. Briefly,

$$\underset{\theta \to 0}{\text{limit}} \ \frac{\theta}{\sin \theta} = 1$$

and similarly it can be shown that

$$\underset{\theta \to 0}{\text{limit}} \ \frac{\theta}{\tan \theta} = 1$$

Hence when θ is small, $\theta = \sin \theta = \tan \theta$.

From tables, if $\theta = 0.0698$ rad (i.e., $4°$)

$$\sin \theta = 0.0698$$

$$\tan \theta = 0.0699$$

For values of θ less than this, the agreement is much closer and for values greater than $4°$, there is an increasing divergency.

9.2 Addition theorems

From $\qquad \sin (A + B) = \sin A \cos B + \cos A \sin B$

and $\qquad \sin (A - B) = \sin A \cos B - \cos A \sin B$

by addition,

$$\sin (A + B) + \sin (A - B) = 2 \sin A \cos B \qquad (9.1)$$

by subtraction,

$$\sin (A + B) - \sin (A - B) = 2 \cos A \sin B \qquad (9.2)$$

Let $\qquad A + B = S$

and $\qquad A - B = T$

by addition $\qquad 2A \quad\; = S + T$

by subtraction $\qquad 2B = S - T$

hence $\qquad A = \dfrac{S + T}{2}$

and $\qquad B = \dfrac{S - T}{2}$

Substituting in (9.1) and (9.2),

$$\sin S + \sin T = 2 \sin \frac{S + T}{2} \cos \frac{S - T}{2} \qquad (9.3)$$

and
$$\sin S - \sin T = 2 \cos \frac{S + T}{2} \sin \frac{S - T}{2} \qquad (9.4)$$

Similarly

$$\cos S + \cos T = 2 \cos \frac{S + T}{2} \cos \frac{S - T}{2} \qquad (9.5)$$

and
$$\cos S - \cos T = -2 \sin \frac{S + T}{2} \sin \frac{S - T}{2} \qquad (9.6)$$

These results may be more easily memorized in words;

(9.3) Sum of two sines = twice sin (half sum) cos (half diff.)

(9.4) Diff. of two sines = twice cos (half sum) sin (half diff.)

(9.5) Sum of two cosines = twice cos (half sum) cos (half diff.)

(9.6) Diff. of two cosines = minus twice sin (half sum) sin (half diff.)

Example 9.1. Write $\sin 36° + \sin 42°$ as the product of two trigonometrical functions.

$$\sin 36° + \sin 42° = 2 \sin \frac{36° + 42°}{2} \cos \frac{36° - 42°}{2}$$
$$= 2 \sin 39° \cos (-3°)$$
$$= 2 \sin 39° \cos 3° \qquad [\cos (-\theta) = \cos \theta]$$

Example 9.2. Write $2 \cos 40° \cos 80°$ as the sum or difference of two trigonometrical functions.

2 cos 40° cos 80° is in the form of (9.5).

$$\therefore \quad \frac{S + T}{2} = 40 \quad \Big\} \quad \text{by addition,} \quad S = 120°$$

$$\therefore \quad \frac{S - T}{2} = 80 \quad \Big\} \quad \text{by subtraction,} \quad T = -40°$$

$$\therefore \quad 2 \cos 40° \cos 80° = \cos 120° + \cos (-40°)$$
$$= \cos 120° + \cos 40°$$

9.3 Differentiation of sin θ from first principles

The trigonometrical properties of sections 9.1 and 9.2 have a useful application in the differentiation of sin θ from first principles.

Let $y = \sin \theta$ where θ is in radians.

If θ receives a small increment $\delta\theta$ and y a corresponding increment δy, then

$$y + \delta y = \sin (\theta + \delta\theta)$$

subtracting $\quad y \qquad = \sin \theta$

$$\overline{\delta y = \sin (\theta + \delta\theta) - \sin \theta}$$

From (9.4),

$$\sin (\theta + \delta\theta) - \sin \theta = 2 \cos (\theta + \delta\theta/2) \sin \delta\theta/2$$

$$\therefore \quad \delta y = 2 \cos (\theta + \delta\theta/2) \sin \delta\theta/2$$

$$\therefore \quad \frac{\delta y}{\delta\theta} = \frac{2 \cos (\theta + \delta\theta/2) \sin \delta\theta/2}{2 \times \delta\theta/2}$$

$$= \frac{2 \cos (\theta + \delta\theta/2)}{2} \times \frac{\sin \delta\theta/2}{\delta\theta/2}$$

Let $\delta\theta \to 0$. Then $\delta y/\delta\theta \to dy/d\theta$ and from section 9.1,

$$\frac{\sin \delta\theta/2}{\delta\theta/2} \to 1$$

$$\therefore \quad \frac{dy}{d\theta} = \cos \theta$$

It is left as an exercise for the student to follow similar lines in the differentiation of cos θ from first principles.

13

9.4   Integration of functions of the form sin $a\theta$ cos $b\theta$

Example 9.3.   Evaluate $\displaystyle\int_0^{\pi/3} 2 \sin 4\theta \cos 2\theta \, d\theta.$

The function is of the form of the identity (9.3).

$\therefore$ $2 \sin 4\theta \cos 2\theta = \sin 6\theta + \sin 2\theta$

$$\therefore \int_0^{\pi/3} 2 \sin 4\theta \cos 2\theta \, d\theta = \int_0^{\pi/3} (\sin 6\theta + \sin 2\theta) \, d\theta$$

$$= \left[-\frac{\cos 6\theta}{6} - \frac{\cos 2\theta}{2} \right]_0^{\pi/3}$$

$$= \left[-\frac{\cos 2\pi}{6} - \frac{\cos 2\pi/3}{2} \right] - \left[-\frac{\cos 0}{6} - \frac{\cos 0}{2} \right]$$

$$= \left[-\frac{1}{6} + \frac{1}{4} \right] - \left[-\frac{1}{6} - \frac{1}{2} \right]$$

$$= \frac{3}{4}$$

Example 9.4.   Evaluate $\displaystyle\int_0^{\pi/6} \cos 5\theta \cos 2\theta \, d\theta.$

The function is of the form of the identity (9.5) of 9.2.

$$\cos 5\theta \cos 2\theta = \frac{1}{2}(\cos 7\theta + \cos 3\theta)$$

$$\therefore \int_0^{\pi/6} \cos 5\theta \cos 2\theta \, d\theta = \frac{1}{2} \int_0^{\pi/6} (\cos 7\theta + \cos 3\theta) \, d\theta$$

$$= \frac{1}{2} \left[\frac{\sin 7\theta}{7} + \frac{\sin 3\theta}{3} \right]_0^{\pi/6}$$

$$= \frac{1}{2} \left[\frac{\sin 7\pi/6}{7} + \frac{\sin \pi/2}{3} \right] - \frac{1}{2} [0 + 0]$$

$$= \frac{1}{2} \left[-\frac{1}{14} + \frac{1}{3} \right]$$

$$= \frac{11}{84}$$

9.5   Production of harmonics

The characteristics of a certain valve give a relation between anode current I and grid voltage V expressed by $I = 8 + 3V + \frac{1}{2}V^2$. We assume the normal grid voltage to be $+5$ volts and apply a sinusoidal voltage given by $v = 2 \sin \omega t$ where $\omega = 4000$. Hence the total grid voltage is given by $V = 5 + 2 \sin \omega t$.

$$\therefore I = 8 + 3V + \tfrac{1}{2}V^2$$
$$= 8 + 3(5 + 2 \sin \omega t) + \tfrac{1}{2}(5 + 2 \sin \omega t)^2$$
$$= 8 + 15 + 6 \sin \omega t + \tfrac{1}{2}(25 + 4 \sin^2 \omega t + 20 \sin \omega t)$$
$$= 35 \cdot 5 + 16 \sin \omega t + 2 \sin^2 \omega t$$
$$= 35 \cdot 5 + 16 \sin \omega t + (1 - \cos 2\omega t)$$
$$= 36 \cdot 5 + 16 \sin \omega t - \cos 2\omega t$$

The anode current flowing consists of three components; a d.c. element of 36·5 mA, an alternating current of the fundamental frequency represented by ωt, of amplitude 16 mA, and a component of twice the fundamental frequency, of amplitude 1 mA. This latter term, $\cos 2\omega t$, is given the name 'second harmonic', and is said to distort the output by approximately 6%, i.e., amplitude 1 compared with amplitude 16.

In chapter 1, p. 22, part of Example 1.18, a question on harmonic distortion, was deferred; this can now be discussed.

Example 9.5 (from Example 1.18, p. 22). The current i in a microphone circuit at any instant t may be regarded as, $i = v/(r_0 + r_1 \sin \omega t)$ where v, r_0, and r_1 are positive constants and r_1 is much smaller than r_0. Show that, to a first approximation,

$$i = \frac{v}{r_0}\left(1 - \frac{r_1}{r_0}\sin \omega t\right)$$

and that to a second approximation, the amplitude of the second harmonic distortion present in the microphone circuit is $50 r_1/r_0\%$ of the amplitude of the fundamental.   C.G.L.I. T.T.

$$i = \frac{v}{r_0 + r_1 \sin \omega t}$$

$$= \frac{v}{r_0\left(1 + \dfrac{r_1}{r_0}\sin \omega t\right)}$$

$$= \frac{v}{r_0}\left(1 + \frac{r_1}{r_0}\sin \omega t\right)^{-1}$$

$$= \frac{v}{r_0}\left[1 + (-1)\frac{r_1}{r_0}\sin \omega t + \frac{(-1)(-1-1)}{1 \times 2}\left(\frac{r_1}{r_0}\sin \omega t\right)^2 + \cdots \right]$$

$$= \frac{v}{r_0}\left[1 - \frac{r_1}{r_0}\sin \omega t + \frac{r_1^2}{r_0^2}\sin^2 \omega t - \cdots \right]$$

$$= \frac{v}{r_0}\left[1 - \frac{r_1}{r_0}\sin \omega t + \frac{r_1^2}{r_0^2} \times \frac{1}{2}(1 - \cos 2\omega t) - \cdots \right]$$

$$= \frac{v}{r_0}\left[1 - \frac{r_1}{r_0}\sin \omega t + \frac{r_1^2}{2r_0^2} - \frac{r_1^2}{2r_0^2}\cos 2\omega t - \cdots \right]$$

The amplitude of the fundamental term is vr_1/r_0^2 and the amplitude of the second harmonic term is $vr_1^2/2r_0^3$.

Hence, the percentage distortion present due to the second harmonic is:

$$\frac{vr_1^2/2r_0^3}{vr_1/r_0^2} \times 100$$

$$= \frac{vr_1^2}{2r_0^3} \times \frac{r_0^2}{vr_1} \times 100$$

$$= \frac{50r_1}{r_0} \%$$

Example 9.6. Plot the graph of $y = 4 \sin \theta + \sin 3\theta$ for values of θ from 0 to 2π radians.

The function shows two terms, in the form of a fundamental variable θ and its third harmonic 3θ; θ has been chosen in preference to ωt or $2\pi ft$ for simplicity of plotting.

θ:	0	$\frac{\pi}{6}$	$\frac{\pi}{3}$	$\frac{\pi}{2}$	$\frac{2\pi}{3}$	$\frac{5\pi}{6}$	π
3θ:	0	$\frac{\pi}{2}$	π	$\frac{3\pi}{2}$	2π	$\frac{5\pi}{2}$	3π
$4 \sin \theta$:	0	2	3·47	4	3·47	2	0
$\sin 3\theta$:	0	1	0	-1	0	1	0
y:	0	3	3·47	3	3·47	3	0

θ:	$\dfrac{7\pi}{6}$	$\dfrac{4\pi}{3}$	$\dfrac{3\pi}{2}$	$\dfrac{5\pi}{3}$	$\dfrac{11\pi}{6}$	2π
3θ:	$\dfrac{7\pi}{2}$	4π	$\dfrac{9\pi}{2}$	5π	$\dfrac{11\pi}{2}$	6π
$4\sin\theta$:	-2	$-3{\cdot}47$	-4	$-3{\cdot}47$	-2	0
$\sin 3\theta$	-1	0	1	0	-1	0
y:	-3	$-3{\cdot}47$	-3	$-3{\cdot}47$	-3	0

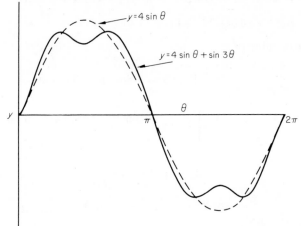

Fig. 9.2

It is to be noted that the maximum value of $4\sin\theta$ has been slightly reduced by the inclusion of the third harmonic and that the shape of the wave has become closer to a flat-topped or rectangular type of wave. This leads to a useful comparison between the mean and r.m.s. values of $4\sin\theta$ and $4\sin\theta + \sin 3\theta$.

(a) Mean value of $4\sin\theta + \sin 3\theta$

$$= \frac{1}{\pi}\int_0^\pi (4\sin\theta + \sin 3\theta)\,\mathrm{d}\theta$$

$$= \frac{1}{\pi}\left[-4\cos\theta - \frac{\cos 3\theta}{3}\right]_0^\pi$$

$$= \frac{1}{\pi}\left[4 + \frac{1}{3}\right] - \frac{1}{\pi}\left[-4 - \frac{1}{3}\right]$$

$$= \frac{8}{\pi} + \frac{2}{3\pi}$$

which compares with $8/\pi$ for the mean value of $4 \sin \theta$. Hence the inclusion of the third harmonic has increased the mean value by approximately 8%.

(b) R.M.S. values

$$y = 4 \sin \theta + \sin 3\theta$$
$$\therefore \ y^2 = 16 \sin^2 \theta + 8 \sin \theta \sin 3\theta + \sin^2 3\theta$$

The term $8 \sin \theta \sin 3\theta$ is in the form of identity (9.6) of section 9.2.

$$\therefore \ y^2 = 16 \times \tfrac{1}{2}(1 - \cos 2\theta) + 4(\cos 2\theta - \cos 4\theta) + \tfrac{1}{2}(1 - \cos 6\theta)$$

$$= 8 \cdot 5 - 4 \cos 2\theta - 4 \cos 4\theta - \tfrac{1}{2} \cos 6\theta$$

$\therefore$ Mean value of y^2

$$= \frac{1}{\pi} \int_0^\pi (8 \cdot 5 - 4 \cos 2\theta - 4 \cos 4\theta - \tfrac{1}{2} \cos 6\theta) \, d\theta$$

$$= \frac{1}{\pi} \left[8 \cdot 5\theta - \frac{4 \sin 2\theta}{2} - \frac{4 \sin 4\theta}{4} - \frac{1}{2} \frac{\sin 6\theta}{6} \right]_0^\pi$$

$$= \frac{1}{\pi} \left[8 \cdot 5\pi \right] - 0$$

$$= 8 \cdot 5$$

Hence   R.M.S. value of $y = \sqrt{8 \cdot 5} = 2 \cdot 915$

and   R.M.S. value of $4 \sin \theta = 4/\sqrt{2} = 2 \cdot 828$

Hence the inclusion of the third harmonic has increased the r.m.s. value by 3% approximately.

9.6   Proof of Simpson's rule

The trapezoidal rule divides an area under a curve into strips, each of which is then assumed to be a trapezium. (See Fig. 9.3.)

The approximation is, that the upper boundary of each strip is a straight line. Simpson's rule suggests that a closer approximation can be produced if it is assumed that the upper boundary is part of a parabola. (See Fig. 9.4.)

Let PMQ be an arc of a parabola whose equation is $y = ax^2 + bx + c$; we take the point M on the y-axis for convenience of calculation, and the points P and Q at $x = -h$ and $x = +h$, giving equal width to the two strips of area. Hence the ordinates y_1, y_2, and y_3 are given by the relations,

$$y_1 = ah^2 - bh + c \qquad (9.7)$$
$$y_2 = c \qquad (9.8)$$
$$y_3 = ah^2 + bh + c \qquad (9.9)$$

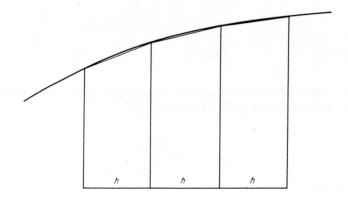

Fig. 9.3

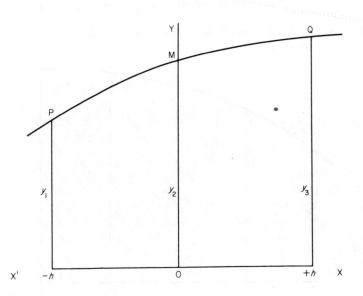

Fig. 9.4

By integration, the total area of the two strips is

$$\int_{-h}^{+h} (ax^2 + bx + c)\,dx = \left[\frac{ax^3}{3} + \frac{bx^2}{2} + cx\right]_{-h}^{+h}$$

$$= \left[\frac{ah^3}{3} + \frac{bh^2}{2} + ch\right] - \left[-\frac{ah^3}{3} + \frac{bh^2}{2} - ch\right]$$

$$= \frac{2ah^3}{3} + 2ch$$

$$= \frac{h}{3}(2ah^2 + 6c) \tag{9.10}$$

We now relate the terms of the bracket to the ordinates y_1, y_2, and y_3 by use of the equations (9.7), (9.8), and (9.9).

From (9.7) and (9.9),

$$y_1 + y_3 = 2ah^2 + 2c$$
$$\therefore \; y_1 + y_3 + 4c = 2ah^2 + 6c$$

From (9.8),

$$y_1 + 4y_2 + y_3 = 2ah^2 + 6c \tag{9.11}$$

From (9.10) and (9.11),

$$\text{Total area of the two strips} = \frac{h}{3}(y_1 + 4y_2 + y_3) \tag{9.12}$$

We now repeat the form of the expression on the r.h.s. of (9.12) for the next two consecutive strips of width h. (See Fig. 9.5.)

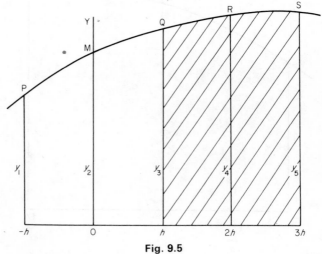

Fig. 9.5

$$\text{Area shaded} = \frac{h}{3}(y_3 + 4y_4 + y_5)$$

$$\therefore \text{ Total area of four strips} = \frac{h}{3}(y_1 + 4y_2 + y_3) + \frac{h}{3}(y_3 + 4y_4 + y_5)$$

$$= \frac{h}{3}\left[y_1 + 4(y_2 + y_4) + 2y_3 + y_5\right]$$

It is left as an exercise for the student to add the area of the next two strips and to verify that,

$$\text{Total area} = \frac{\text{width of strip}}{3}\left[\text{1st + last ordinate}\right.$$
$$+4(\text{sum of even ordinates})$$
$$\left.+2(\text{sum of odd ordinates})\right]$$

The conditions applying to the use of Simpson's rule are that the area should be divided into an even number of strips of equal width, giving an odd number of ordinates. The first and last ordinates, although odd in position, are excluded from that part of the formula requiring 'twice the sum of odd ordinates'. In Fig. 9.6, the first and last ordinates are each zero and this is the value to be used in the formula.

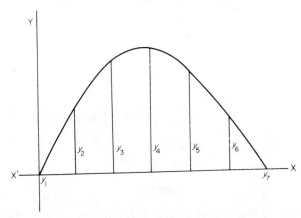

Fig. 9.6

Example 9.7. Evaluate $\int_0^1 dx/(5 - 3x)$ and verify the result by using Simpson's rule with five ordinates.

C.G.L.I. T.T.

Let $y = 1/(5 - 3x)$, then

$$\int_0^1 \frac{dx}{5 - 3x} = \text{area under curve}$$

$$\therefore \quad \text{area} = \left[-\tfrac{1}{3}\log(5 - 3x)\right]_0^1$$

$$= -\tfrac{1}{3}[\log 2 - \log 5]$$

$$= \tfrac{1}{3}[\log 5 - \log 2]$$

$$= \tfrac{1}{3}\log \tfrac{5}{2}$$

$$= \tfrac{1}{3} \times 0{\cdot}9163$$

$$= 0{\cdot}3054$$

From the graph $y = 1/(5 - 3x)$, using Simpson's rule, we require five equally spaced ordinates between $x = 0$ and $x = 1$, giving four strips each of width 0·25.

$$y = \frac{1}{5 - 3x}$$

x	0	0·25	0·5	0·75	1·0
y	0·2	0·235	0·286	0·364	0·5
	y_1	y_2	y_3	y_4	y_5

$$\text{Area under curve} = \frac{h}{3}\left[y_1 + y_5 + 4(y_2 + y_4) + 2y_3\right]$$

$$= \frac{0{\cdot}25}{3}\left[0{\cdot}7 + 4(0{\cdot}599) + 2(0{\cdot}286)\right]$$

$$= \frac{0{\cdot}25}{3}\left[0{\cdot}7 + 2{\cdot}396 + 0{\cdot}572\right]$$

$$= \frac{0{\cdot}25}{3}\left[3{\cdot}668\right]$$

$$= 0{\cdot}3057$$

Comparison of the results by the two methods shows very close agreement, which would be improved by using a larger number of strips.

9.7 Use of Simpson's rule for approximate integration

There are instances in which the general integration of a function is difficult or impossible, and where a definite integral only is required of these functions, it is possible to apply Simpson's rule to find the area under the corresponding graph; this is referred to as numerical integration.

Example 9.8. Evaluate $\int_0^1 e^{-x^2} \, dx$ using Simpson's rule, taking nine ordinates.

Let $y = e^{-x^2}$

x:	0	0·125	0·25	0·375	0·5	0·625	0·75	0·875	1·0
x^2:	0	0·0156	0·0625	0·141	0·25	0·391	0·562	0·765	1·0
$y = e^{-x^2}$:	1	0·985	0·940	0·869	0·779	0·676	0·570	0·465	0·368
Ord. no.:	y_1	y_2	y_3	y_4	y_5	y_6	y_7	y_8	y_9

$\therefore$ Area $= \dfrac{h}{3} \left[y_1 + y_9 + 4(y_2 + y_4 + y_6 + y_8) + 2(y_3 + y_5 + y_7) \right]$

$$= \frac{0 \cdot 125}{3} \left[1 + 0 \cdot 368 + 4 \begin{pmatrix} 0 \cdot 985 \\ 0 \cdot 869 \\ 0 \cdot 676 \\ 0 \cdot 465 \end{pmatrix} + 2 \begin{pmatrix} 0 \cdot 940 \\ 0 \cdot 779 \\ 0 \cdot 570 \end{pmatrix} \right]$$

$$= \frac{0 \cdot 125}{3} \left[1 \cdot 368 + 4(2 \cdot 995) + 2(2 \cdot 289) \right]$$

$$= \frac{0 \cdot 125}{3} \left[1 \cdot 368 + 11 \cdot 980 + 4 \cdot 578 \right]$$

$$= \frac{0 \cdot 125}{3} \left[17 \cdot 926 \right]$$

$$= 0 \cdot 747$$

$$\therefore \int_0^1 e^{-x^2} \, dx = 0 \cdot 747$$

9.8   Integration by substitution

Apart from simple functions of the form x^n, for which there is a mechanical rule for integration, most other functions rely on 'standard forms' for integration. This often means that they must be re-shaped algebraically or trigonometrically before using the methods of calculus. The means of re-shaping various functions are numerous and we shall deal here with only a few.

(a) In section 3.2 of chapter 3, it has been shown that, if $y = \log f(x)$, then

$$\frac{dy}{dx} = \frac{f'(x)}{f(x)}$$

If then, we are required to integrate a function in a fractional form, whose numerator is, or can be made into, the differential coefficient of the denominator, the integral must be of a logarithmic form.

Example 9.9. Find the integral of $\dfrac{x - 3}{x^2 - 6x + 8}$.

$$I = \int \frac{(x - 3)\,dx}{x^2 - 6x + 8}$$

Let $u = x^2 - 6x + 8$

$$\therefore \frac{du}{dx} = 2x - 6$$

$$\therefore \tfrac{1}{2}\,du = (x - 3)\,dx$$

$$\therefore I = \int \frac{1}{2}\frac{du}{u}$$

$$= \frac{1}{2} \log u$$

$$\frac{1}{2} \log (x^2 - 6x + 8) + C$$

Example 9.10. Find the integral of $\tan \theta$.

$$I = \int \tan \theta\, d\theta$$

$$= \int \frac{\sin \theta}{\cos \theta}\, d\theta$$

Let $u = \cos \theta$

$$\therefore \frac{du}{d\theta} = -\sin \theta$$

$$\therefore -du = \sin \theta\, d\theta$$

$$\therefore I = \int -\frac{du}{u}$$

$$= -\log u$$
$$= -\log (\cos \theta)$$
$$= \log (\cos \theta)^{-1}$$
$$= \log (\sec \theta) + C$$

(b) An expression of the form $(ax^m + b)^n$ is classified and differentiated as a function of a function. It does not follow that an exact reverse process will enable us to integrate such functions; each expression must be considered separately.

Example 9.11. Find the integral of $(3x + 2)^7 \, dx$

$$I = \int (3x + 2)^7 \, dx \qquad\qquad \text{Let } u = 3x + 2$$

$$\therefore \; \frac{du}{dx} = 3$$

$$\therefore \; \frac{1}{3} \, du = dx$$

$$\therefore \; I = \int u^7 \frac{1}{3} \, du \qquad\qquad\qquad (9.13)$$

$$= \frac{1}{3} \frac{u^8}{8}$$

$$= \frac{1}{24} (3x + 2)^8 + C$$

Example 9.12. Find the integral of $2x^2(x^3 + 8)^{1/2} \, dx$

$$I = \int 2x^2(x^3 + 8)^{1/2} \, dx \qquad\qquad \text{Let } u = x^3 + 8$$

$$\therefore \; \frac{du}{dx} = 3x^2$$

$$\therefore \; \frac{2}{3} \frac{du}{dx} = 2x^2$$

$$\therefore \; \frac{2}{3} \, du = 2x^2 \, dx$$

$$\therefore I = \int u^{1/2} \frac{2}{3}\, \mathrm{d}u \qquad\qquad (9.14)$$

$$= \frac{2}{3} \frac{u^{3/2}}{3/2}$$

$$= \frac{4}{9}(x^3 + 8)^{3/2} + C$$

It should be noted that the choice of substitution in Examples 9.11 and 9.12 has permitted a complete change of the variable x, including the operator $\mathrm{d}x$, to a function of the variable u. (See (9.13) and (9.14).)

(c) Trigonometrical substitution

Familiarity with the trigonometrical identities is of material assistance in the correct choice of substitution.

Example 9.13. Find the integral of $\sqrt{(4 - x^2)}\, \mathrm{d}x$

$$I = \int \sqrt{(4 - x^2)}\, \mathrm{d}x \qquad\qquad \text{Let } x = 2 \sin \theta$$

$$\therefore\ x^2 = 4 \sin^2 \theta$$

$$\therefore\ 4 - x^2 = 4 - 4 \sin^2 \theta$$

$$= 4(1 - \sin^2 \theta)$$

$$= 4 \cos^2 \theta$$

$$\therefore\ \sqrt{(4 - x^2)} = 2 \cos \theta$$

$$\text{From } x = 2 \sin \theta$$

$$\therefore\ \frac{\mathrm{d}x}{\mathrm{d}\theta} = 2 \cos \theta$$

$$\therefore\ \mathrm{d}x = 2 \cos \theta\, \mathrm{d}\theta$$

$$\therefore\ I = \int 2 \cos \theta\, 2 \cos \theta\, \mathrm{d}\theta$$

$$= 2 \int 2 \cos^2 \theta\, \mathrm{d}\theta$$

$$= 2 \int (1 + \cos 2\theta)\, \mathrm{d}\theta$$

$$= 2 \left[\theta + \frac{\sin 2\theta}{2} \right] + C$$

Since the given function was expressed in terms of x, our answer should be converted into those terms by means of the substitution used, i.e., $x = 2 \sin \theta$. In the more frequently occurring conditions of practical problems however, a definite integral requiring a numerical answer, is sufficient. In this case, the given limits, referring to the variable x, are converted to the corresponding values for the new variable θ and the integral evaluated. (See Example 9.14.)

Example 9.14. Calculate the area of a circle of radius 5 cm by a method of integration.

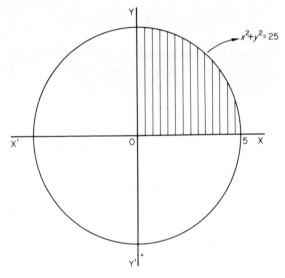

Fig. 9.7

We locate the circle conveniently, with its centre at the origin of rectangular co-ordinates. Hence its equation is $x^2 + y^2 = 25$. We shall calculate the area shown shaded, between limits for x from 0 to 5, and multiply the result by 4.

From $x^2 + y^2 = 25$

$$\therefore y^2 = 25 - x^2$$

$$\therefore y = \sqrt{(25 - x^2)}$$

$$\therefore \text{Area} = 4 \int_0^5 \sqrt{(25 - x^2)}\, dx \qquad\qquad \text{Let } x = 5 \sin \theta$$

$$\therefore x^2 = 25 \sin^2 \theta$$

$$\therefore \ 25 - x^2 = 25(1 - \sin^2 \theta)$$
$$= 25 \cos^2 \theta$$
$$\therefore \ \sqrt{(25 - x^2)} = 5 \cos \theta$$
$$\text{From } x = 5 \sin \theta$$
$$\therefore \ \frac{dx}{d\theta} = 5 \cos \theta$$
$$\therefore \ dx = 5 \cos \theta \ d\theta$$
$$\therefore \ \text{Area} = 4 \int 5 \cos \theta \ 5 \cos \theta \ d\theta$$

It should be noted that the limits for x of 0 and 5 are no longer applicable to this integral which is in terms of the variable θ; the corresponding limits are found from the chosen substitution.

$$\text{If } x = 0, \quad 0 = 5 \sin \theta$$
$$\therefore \ 0 = \theta$$
$$\text{If } x = 5, \quad 5 = 5 \sin \theta$$
$$\therefore \ 1 = \sin \theta$$
$$\therefore \ \frac{\pi}{2} = \theta$$

$$\therefore \ \text{Area} = 100 \int_0^{\pi/2} \cos^2 \theta \ d\theta$$
$$= 100 \int_0^{\pi/2} \frac{1}{2}(1 + \cos 2\theta) \ d\theta$$
$$= 50 \left[\theta + \frac{\sin 2\theta}{2} \right]_0^{\pi/2}$$
$$= 50 \left[\frac{\pi}{2} + 0 \right] - 50[0]$$
$$= 25\pi \ \text{cm}^2$$

9.9   Volumes of revolution

If the rectangular area PQRS is rotated through 360° about the axis AA, it is said to produce the volume of a cylinder of length PS and radius PQ. We apply this principle to an area under a given curve.

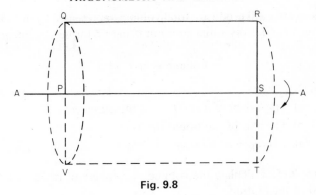

Fig. 9.8

The area to be rotated is bounded by the given curve, $y = f(x)$, the x-axis and the ordinates $x = a$ and $x = b$; the axis of rotation is the x-axis. We consider a typical strip, BCDE, of the area; typical, meaning that the whole area can be divided into strips of a generally similar shape.

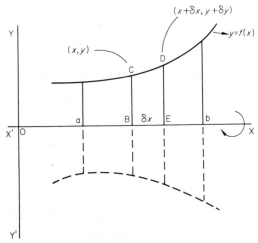

Fig. 9.9

Let the co-ordinates of C be (x, y) and let the co-ordinates of D be $(x + \delta x, y + \delta y)$. Hence

$$CB = y \quad \text{and} \quad BE = \delta x$$

If δx is very small, the area BCDE can be regarded as rectangular, and in one complete rotation about the x-axis will produce the volume of a disc. Hence

$$\delta V = \pi y^2 \, \delta x$$

14

The given area will produce a total volume, represented by the addition of all such similar discs, the addition being performed by integration.

$$\therefore \text{ Volume} = \pi \int_a^b y^2 \, dx$$

Notes. (a) The values of a and b are x measurements.

(b) The axis of rotation is the x-axis.

(c) y is replaced by $f(x)$.

Example 9.15. Calculate the volume of a sphere of radius 4 cm by a method of integration.

A sphere can be considered as the result of rotating a circle about a diameter. We locate the circle conveniently with its centre at the origin of rectangular co-ordinates.

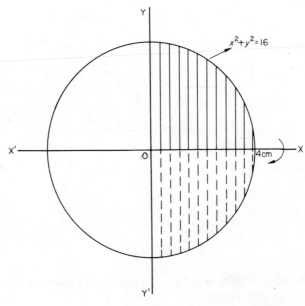

Fig. 9.10

Hence its equation is $x^2 + y^2 = 16$.

We shall calculate the volume produced by the rotation of a quadrant of the circle, i.e., a hemisphere, and multiply the result by 2.

From $x^2 + y^2 = 16$

$$\therefore y^2 = 16 - x^2$$

$$\therefore V = 2\pi \int_0^4 (16 - x^2)\, dx$$

$$= 2\pi \left[16x - \frac{x^3}{3} \right]_0^4$$

$$= 2\pi \left[64 - \frac{64}{3} \right] - 0$$

$$= 2\pi \times \frac{2}{3} \times 64$$

$$= \tfrac{1}{3}.4^4 \pi \text{ cm}^3$$

Example 9.16. Calculate the volume of a cone of height h and radius r.

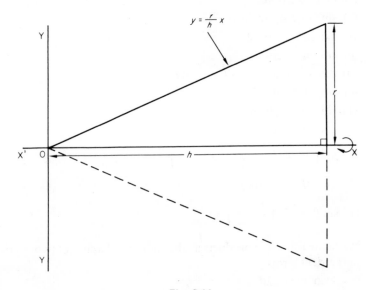

$y = \frac{r}{h} x$

Fig. 9.11

An area bounded by a straight-line graph, the x-axis, and an ordinate of length r at $x = h$, is rotated about the x-axis to produce the volume of a cone. We locate the straight-line graph conveniently to pass through the origin.

Hence its equation is,

$$y = \frac{r}{h} x$$

$$\therefore \ V = \pi \int_0^h \frac{r^2}{h^2} x^2 \, dx$$

$$= \pi \left[\frac{r^2}{h^2} \frac{x^3}{3} \right]_0^h$$

$$= \pi \left[\frac{r^2}{h^2} \frac{h^3}{3} \right]$$

$$= \tfrac{1}{3}\pi r^2 h$$

EXERCISE 9.1

1. Write the following expressions as the products of two trigonometrical functions.

   (a) $\sin 2\omega_1 t + \sin 2\omega_2 t$

   (b) $\sin 2\pi F t - \sin 2\pi f t$

   (c) $\cos \omega t + \cos \phi t$

   (d) $\cos (\omega t + \alpha) - \cos (\omega t + \phi)$

   (e) $\sin 2\theta + \sin 6\theta$

   (f) $\sin 3\omega t - \sin \omega t$

   (g) $\cos 4\theta - \cos 2\theta$

   (h) $\cos \left(3\theta + \dfrac{\pi}{3} \right) + \cos \left(2\theta - \dfrac{\pi}{3} \right)$

   (i) $\sin 50t + \sin 100t$

   (j) $\sin \theta - \sin \left(\dfrac{\pi}{2} - \theta \right)$

2. Write the following products as the sum or difference of two trigonometrical terms.

   (a) $2 \sin 4\theta \cos 2\theta$

   (b) $2 \cos 6\omega t \sin 2\omega t$

   (c) $2 \cos 100t \cos 50t$

   (d) $-2 \sin 8\theta \sin 2\theta$

   (e) $4 \sin \left(\omega t + \dfrac{\pi}{3} \right) \cos \left(\omega t - \dfrac{\pi}{3} \right)$

(f) $\cos 2\pi Ft \cos 2\pi ft$

(g) $\sin \omega_1 t \sin \omega_2 t$

(h) $\frac{1}{2} \sin \left(2\theta + \frac{\pi}{2} \right) \cos \left(\theta - \frac{\pi}{2} \right)$

(i) $\cos 75° \cos 15°$

(j) $\cos (2\alpha + \beta) \sin (\alpha + 2\beta)$

3. Evaluate without using tables,

(a) $\sin 75° - \sin 15°$

(b) $\cos 150° - \cos 75°$

4. Write down the formulae for $\sin (A + B)$ and $\sin (A - B)$ in terms of the trigonometrical ratios for the angles A and B. Hence complete the following identity:

$$\sin 2\pi Ft \cos 2\pi ft = \frac{1}{2} \left[\sin 2\pi(\quad)t + \sin 2\pi(\quad)t \right]$$

E.M.E.U. (part Qn.)

5. Solve the equation, $\cos 5x = \cos x$, giving roots between $0°$ and $360°$.

6. Solve the equation, $\sin 3x + \sin x = 0$, giving roots between $0°$ and $360°$.

7. A voltage given by $v = 4 + \sin 3\omega t$ is applied to a valve whose characteristic is represented by $i = 2v + 4v^2$. Calculate the frequencies and amplitudes of the components of the current.

8. Plot the graph of $y = 2 \sin \theta + \sin 2\theta$ for values of θ from 0 to 2π radians. Find the mean value and the r.m.s. value of y, (a) by Simpson's rule, (b) by calculus.

9. A modulated signal has a voltage given by,

$$v = (\sin \omega t + \tfrac{1}{3} \sin 3\omega t) \sin 15\omega t$$

Use the trigonometrical addition theorems to show the four component sinusoidal voltages and state their frequencies.

10. Calculate the mean value of a current i given by $i = \cos 10t \cos 30t$, for values of t from 0 to 0·1 sec.

11. (a) In a 12-hr period a mains-operated equipment takes a peak load of 20 A (r.m.s.) for 4 hr, while for the remaining 8 hr, only 5 A is taken. Calculate the r.m.s. current taken over the 12 hr.

(b) The voltage across a circuit at a time t sec is given by,

$$v = 5 + 3 \sin \omega t + \cos 3\omega t$$

Sketch this wave-form from $t = 0$ to $t = 2\pi/\omega$, and calculate the r.m.s. value of this voltage over the period 0 to π/ω sec.

C.G.L.I. T.T.

12. Evaluate (a) $\displaystyle\int_3^6 (3x + 7)^{3/2}\, dx$

(b) $\displaystyle\int_0^{\pi/2} \sin 3x \cos 2x\, dx$

C.G.L.I. T.T. (part Qn.)

13. Evaluate (a) $\displaystyle\int_0^1 \frac{x\, dx}{1 + x^2}$

(b) $\displaystyle\int_0^{\pi/2} (\sin 3x + \cos 5x)^2\, dx$

C.G.L.I. T.T. (part Qn.)

14. Calculate the area bounded by the curve $y = \tan x$, the x-axis, and the ordinates $x = \pi/6$ and $x = 3\pi/8$.

15. Use Simpson's rule, taking nine ordinates, to evaluate

$$\int_0^2 \frac{36}{1 + x^3}\, dx$$

16. Calculate the area bounded by the curve, $y = \sin\theta\,(1 + \cos\theta)$, the θ-axis, and the ordinates $\theta = 0$ and $\theta = \pi/2$ radians, (a) by Simpson's rule, using seven ordinates, (b) by integration.

17. Evaluate $\displaystyle\int_0^3 \sqrt{(9 - x^2)}\, dx$

18. Evaluate $\displaystyle\int_0^5 \frac{1}{\sqrt{(25 - x^2)}}\, dx$

19. Calculate the area of the minor segment of a circle of radius 6 cm cut off by a chord which is 2 cm from the centre of the circle.

20. The area bounded by the curve $y = 4x - x^2$ and the x-axis is rotated through one revolution about the x-axis. Sketch the curve and calculate the volume produced.

21. A frustum of a cone has a length of 10 cm and radii of ends 2 cm and 4 cm. Calculate its volume, using a method of integration.

22. A double convex lens is formed by the rotation about the x-axis of the area enclosed between the curves, $4x = y^2 - 4$ and $8x = 4 - y^2$. Sketch these curves and find the volume of the lens.

10. Complex numbers

10.1 Introduction

Two alternating voltages, 100 V and 50 V, are in phase; what is the total voltage? (100 + 50 = 150 V)

Two alternating voltages, 100 V and 50 V oppose each other, i.e. at a phase angle of 180°; what is the total voltage? (100 − 50 = 50 V).

The simplicity of these answers depends on the voltages acting 'in line,' i.e., in phase. This expression now implies the vectorial or directional sense of the two magnitudes, 100 V and 50 V (Fig. 10.1).

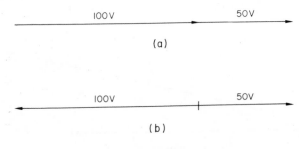

(a)

(b)

Fig. 10.1

Two alternating voltages, 100 V and 50 V, act in a circuit so that the 50 V leads the 100 V by 90°. What is the resultant voltage? The calculation must now involve a diagram, Pythagoras' theorem and simple trigonometry (Fig. 10.2) and references to two sets of tables.

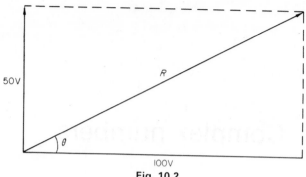

Fig. 10.2

$$R = \sqrt{(100^2 + 50^2)}$$
$$= \sqrt{12,500}$$
$$= 111 \cdot 8 \text{ V}$$
$$\theta = \tan^{-1}\left(\tfrac{50}{100}\right)$$
$$= \tan^{-1}\left(\tfrac{1}{2}\right)$$
$$= 26° \ 34'$$

Resultant voltage, $111 \cdot 8$ V leading the 100 V by $26° \ 34'$.

Two voltages 100 V and 50 V act in a circuit so that the 50 V leads the 100 V by $40°$. What is the resultant voltage? (Fig. 10.3).

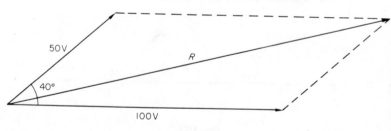

Fig. 10.3

The calculation now involves either scale drawing, which is slow and not very accurate, or the resolution and compounding of components at right-angles, or the use of cosine and sine rules of trigonometry. Our methods of solution are becoming too slow and laborious and, at many stages, do not reflect the physical meaning of the effects of such circuit components as inductance and capacitance. A form of algebra is required whose symbols will represent these effects and whose principles will allow the compounding of the effects by simple addition, subtraction, multiplication, and division.

Cartesian co-ordinates

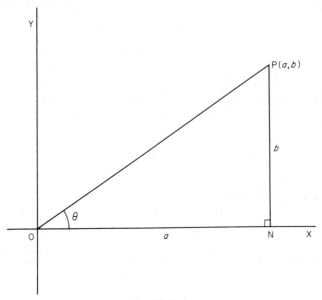

Fig. 10.4

The position of the point P measured graphically in cartesian co-ordinates is given symbolically by (a, b) and we must constantly bear in mind that a is measured horizontally and b vertically; our symbols do not show this.

10.2   Complex numbers

The difficulties expressed above can be overcome if we prefix all vertical measurements by the symbol 'j'. The line OP is then completely defined by the expression $a + jb$. Hence if OP is a vector quantity, its magnitude is $\sqrt{(a^2 + b^2)}$ and its direction is given by $\theta = \tan^{-1}(b/a)$, where θ is the angle made with the positive direction of the x-axis ($\triangle$OPN, Fig. 10.4). In the language of complex numbers, the magnitude $\sqrt{(a^2 + b^2)}$ is called the modulus and the direction θ the argument. We must now investigate the mathematical meaning of this new symbol j, and the mathematical laws of complex numbers. It will be seen that the definition of j gives it the property which, so far, we have assumed, namely that it can represent a measurement at right-angles to a given reference direction, the x-axis, for instance. Historically, the necessity of representing measurements at right-angles to a given reference direction was first suggested by Argand in dealing with the solutions of certain quadratic equations.

If

$$x^2 - 9 = 0$$
$$\therefore x^2 = 9$$
$$\therefore x = \pm 3$$

The real values, $+3$ and -3, could be represented by measurements of 3 units in opposite directions along the same axis.

If

$$x^2 + 1 = 0$$
$$\therefore x^2 = -1$$

Since no real number, when squared, gives a result of -1, then the solution, $x = \pm\sqrt{-1}$, was considered to be imaginary and given the symbol 'i'. Argand first suggested that this number, and others arising from it, such as $\sqrt{-9}$, equal to $\pm 3\sqrt{-1}$, should be represented diagrammatically along an axis perpendicular to the real number axis (Fig. 10.5).

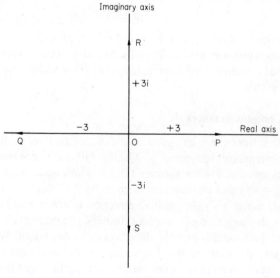

Fig. 10.5

Having established the two axes at right-angles by definition, we must show that the value $\sqrt{-1}$, i.e., i, will provide a functional relationship between them.

In Fig. 10.5,

$$OR = i \times OP$$

and

$$OQ = -1 \times OP = i^2 \times OP$$

$$\therefore \ OQ = i \times OR$$

Similarly

$$OS = i \times OQ$$

The imaginary value 'i' $(= \sqrt{-1})$, therefore, has the property of rotating a vector through 90°. It is ideally suited therefore, to the representation of the leads and lags of 90° occurring in electrical circuits containing inductance and capacitance; the symbol 'j' has been adopted in place of 'i' to prevent confusion with electrical current.

10.3 Powers of j

If

$$j = \sqrt{-1}$$

then

$$j^2 = (\sqrt{-1})^2 = -1$$

$$j^3 = (\sqrt{-1})^2(\sqrt{-1}) = -j$$

$$j^4 = (j^2)^2 = (-1)^2 = +1$$

and so on

10.4 Argand diagram or complex number plane; vectors

A complex number written as $a + jb$, is composed of a real part a and an imaginary part jb. Figure 10.6 illustrates four complex numbers, A $(3 + j2)$, B $(-2 + j3)$, C $(-1 - j2)$, and D $(2 - j3)$.

If A is the point $3 + j2$, it is equally true to say that $3 + j2$ represents the vector OA whose horizontal and vertical components are 3 and 2 respectively.

Hence   Magnitude of OA $= \sqrt{(2^2 + 3^2)}$

and   Direction of OA $= \theta = \tan^{-1}(\frac{2}{3})$

By the definition of a complex number, it is clear that if two complex numbers are equal, then their real parts are equal and their imaginary parts are equal.

If $$a + jb = c + jd$$

then $$a = c$$

and $$b = d$$

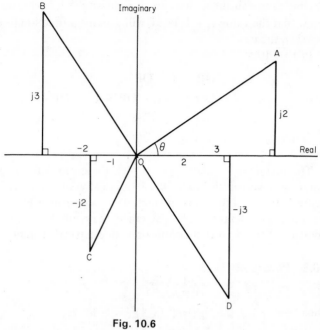

Fig. 10.6

10.5 Multiplication by j

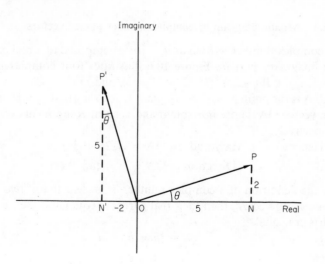

Fig. 10.7

Consider the multiplication, $j(5 + 2j)$.

$$j(5 + 2j) = 5j + 2j^2 = 5j - 2 = -2 + 5j$$

The vector OP represents $5 + 2j$, and the vector OP′ represents $-2 + 5j$.

△'s OPN and OP′N′ are congruent (two sides and an included angle)

$$\therefore \; \angle PON = \angle OP'N' = \theta$$
$$\therefore \; \angle P'ON' = 90° - \theta$$
$$\therefore \; \angle POP' = 90°$$

The vector OP has been rotated through 90° by multiplication by j.

10.6   Addition of complex numbers

We shall add the two complex numbers $3 + 2j$ and $2 + 4j$ algebraically, and compare the stages of the process with the corresponding vectors on the Argand diagram (Fig. 10.8).

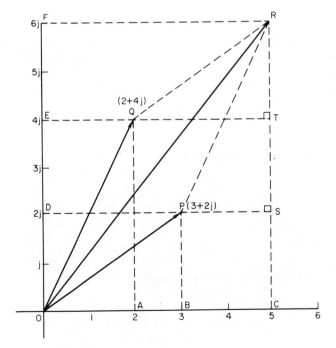

Fig. 10.8

Algebraically,

$$3 + 2j + 2 + 4j = (3 + 2) + (2j + 4j)$$
$$= 5 + 6j \tag{10.1}$$

Let OP represent $3 + 2j$, real part $3 = $ OB, imaginary part $2j = $ OD.
Let OQ represent $2 + 4j$, real part $2 = $ OA, imaginary part $4j = $ OE.
Addition of real parts,

$$OB + OA = OC = 5$$

Addition of imaginary parts,

$$OD + OE = OF = 6j$$

Hence the resultant

$$OR = 5 + 6j \tag{10.2}$$

From $\triangle OQA$ and $\triangle PRS$,

$$OQ = PR = \sqrt{20}$$

From $\triangle QRT$ and $\triangle OPB$,

$$QR = OP = \sqrt{13}$$

Hence OQRP is a parallelogram, the diagonal OR being the conventional resultant of the application of the parallelogram law of forces or vectors.

Comparing (10.1) and (10.2), it can be seen that the algebraic addition of the complex numbers representing two vectors, gives their resultant in complex number form.

10.7   Subtraction of complex numbers

From $6 + 4j$ subtract $2 + 3j$.

$$6 + 4j - (2 + 3j) = 6 + 4j - 2 - 3j$$
$$6 - 2 + 4j - 3j$$
$$= 4 + j$$

10.8   Multiplication of complex numbers

Multiply $(2 + 5j)$ by $(3 + 2j)$.

$$(2 + 5j)(3 + 2j) = 6 + 4j + 15j + 10j^2$$
$$= 6 + 19j - 10 \quad (\text{since } j^2 = -1)$$
$$= -4 + 19j$$

10.9   Division of complex numbers

Divide $(5 - 3j)$ by $(4 + 2j)$ and write the result in the form $a + jb$.

Since the divisor, $(4 + 2j)$, is a term containing a surd, $(j = \sqrt{-1})$, we rationalize the denominator by multiplying by $(4 - 2j)$, which is the 'conjugate' of $4 + 2j$; the two expressions are then factors of the type $(a + b)(a - b)$, the product of which is $a^2 - b^2$.

$$\frac{5 - 3j}{4 + 2j} = \frac{(5 - 3j)(4 - 2j)}{(4 + 2j)(4 - 2j)}$$

$$= \frac{20 - 10j - 12j + 6j^2}{16 - 4j^2}$$

$$= \frac{20 - 22j - 6}{16 + 4}$$

$$= \frac{14 - 22j}{20}$$

$$= \frac{7}{10} - \frac{11j}{10}$$

Summary

1. Complex numbers can be manipulated according to the laws of algebra, using $j = \sqrt{-1}$.
2. The two parts of a complex number can represent two perpendicular components of a vector.

It now remains to apply the algebraic processes to practical terms representing voltage, current, and reactance, etc.

10.10   Symbolic notation

A complex number has been described mathematically as having a real part and an imaginary part. There are no imaginary voltages, currents, or reactances and in place of this term we use the expression 'quadrature' component to represent that vector which is at right-angles to the 'ordinary' (real) vector.

Example 10.1. An impedance vector may be represented by $Z = R \pm jX$ where R is the 'ordinary' or 'in phase' component and the reactance X is the 'quadrature' component arising from a $90°$ lead or lag. Although resistance and reactance are not vector quantities, it is convenient and valid to treat them as such by considering the effect of unit current passing through them. The voltage drop across the impedance will be a vector quantity whose rectangular components will be numerically equal to the components R and X.

Inductive circuit

In an inductive circuit, the voltage drop across the resistance is in phase with the current, whilst the voltage across the inductance leads the current by 90°. Hence, by writing jV_L, we imply this 90° lead over the reference vector I.

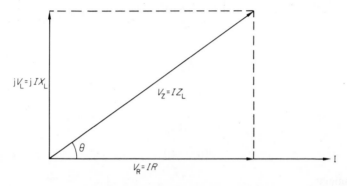

Fig. 10.9

Hence, the voltage across the impedance Z_L is given by

$$V_Z = IZ_L = I(R + jX_L)$$
$$\therefore Z_L = R + jX_L$$

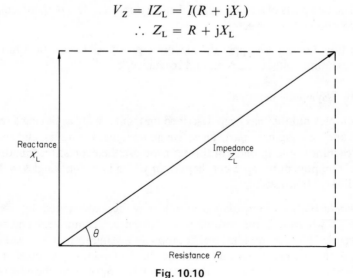

Fig. 10.10

Figure 10.10 will now represent the impedance vector Z_L to a different scale.

The magnitude of the impedance $= \sqrt{(R^2 + X_L^2)}$.

The phase angle between the current in the impedance and the voltage across it $= \theta = \tan^{-1}(X_L/R)$.

Example 10.2. Find the resultant impedance in complex number form of the three impedances in series whose values are $2 + j8$, $5 + j4$, and $10 + j3$. From this resultant, state the magnitude and phase angle.

Since the impedances are in series, the total impedance Z is found by simple addition

$$
\begin{array}{r}
2 + j8 \\
5 + j4 \\
10 + j3 \\
\hline
17 + j15
\end{array}
$$

Magnitude $= \sqrt{(17^2 + 15^2)} = \sqrt{514} = 22\cdot7$ ohm

Phase angle, $\theta = \tan^{-1}(15/17) = \tan^{-1} 0\cdot8824$

$$\therefore \ \theta = 41° \ 26'$$

Since the quadrature component, $j15$, is positive, it can be deduced that the reactance is inductive.

Capacitive circuit

In a capacitive circuit, the voltage across the resistance is in phase with the current, and the voltage across the capacitance lags the current by 90°.

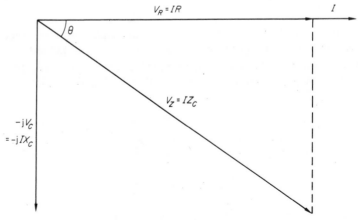

Fig. 10.11

Hence the voltage across the impedance Z_C, is given by,

$$V_z = IZ_C = I(R - jX_C)$$
$$\therefore Z_C = R - jX_C$$

Figure 10.12 will now represent the impedance vector Z_C to a different scale.

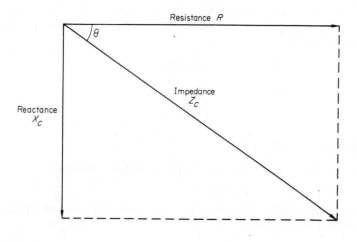

Fig. 10.12

The magnitude of the impedance $= \sqrt{(R^2 + X_C^2)}$.
The phase angle of the impedance $= \theta = \tan^{-1}(-X_C/R)$.

Example 10.3. In a circuit with inductive and capacitive impedances in series, the values are given by $5 + j10$, $10 - j12$, $2 + j3$, and $3 - j4$. Find the resultant impedance in complex number form and represent it on an Argand diagram. Is the resultant impedance inductive or capacitive?

$$
\begin{array}{r}
5 + j10 \\
10 - j12 \\
2 + j3 \\
3 - j4 \\
\hline
\therefore Z = 20 - j3 \\
\hline
\end{array}
$$

Since the quadrature component is negative, the resultant impedance is capacitive.

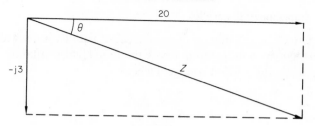

Fig. 10.13

$$\text{Magnitude} = \sqrt{(20^2 + 3^2)} = 20 \cdot 2 \text{ ohm}$$
$$\text{Phase angle } \theta = \tan^{-1}(-3/20) = \tan^{-1}(-0 \cdot 15)$$
$$\therefore \ \theta = -8° \ 32'$$

Example 10.4. The value of an impedance is $10 + j5$ ohm. State whether this is capacitive or inductive and find the resistance and capacitance (or inductance) assuming the frequency to be 50 Hz.

Since the quadrature component, $+j5$, leads the ordinary (resistive) component, the circuit is inductive.

$$\therefore \ \text{Resistance} = 10 \text{ ohm}$$
$$\therefore \ \text{Inductive reactance} = 2\pi fL = 5 \text{ ohm}$$
$$\therefore \ 314L = 5$$
$$\therefore \ L = \frac{5}{314} \text{ H}$$
$$\therefore \ L = 15 \cdot 9 \text{ mH}$$

Example 10.5. The value of an impedance is $20 - j10$ ohm. State the character of this impedance and calculate the value of the resistance and reactance components assuming the frequency to be 50 Hz.

Since the quadrature component, $-j10$, lags the ordinary (resistive) component, the circuit is capacitive.

$$\therefore \ \text{Resistance} = 20 \text{ ohm}$$
$$\therefore \ \text{Capacitive reactance} = \frac{1}{2\pi fC} = 10 \text{ ohm}$$
$$\therefore \ \frac{1}{314C} = 10$$
$$\therefore \ C = \frac{1}{3140} = 0 \cdot 000318 \text{ F}$$
$$\therefore \ C = 318 \ \mu\text{F}$$

15*

10.11   Impedances in parallel

In d.c. work, the calculation of resistances in parallel is derived from the fact that the voltage drop across the individual resistances is the same, namely the applied voltage. Hence

$$\frac{1}{R} = \frac{1}{R_1} + \frac{1}{R_2} + \cdots \tag{10.3}$$

It is convenient to denote the reciprocals in (10.3) by new symbols, descriptions and units.

$$\frac{1}{R} = G = \text{conductance in siemens}$$

Hence, if conductances are connected in parallel, then
$$G = G_1 + G_2 + \cdots$$

Note. The symbol G retains the *meaning* of conductance, i.e., the property of a circuit which allows a current to pass, but its *value* must be modified in a.c. circuits containing reactance.

In a.c. work, with a circuit containing impedances in parallel, a very close comparison can be made.

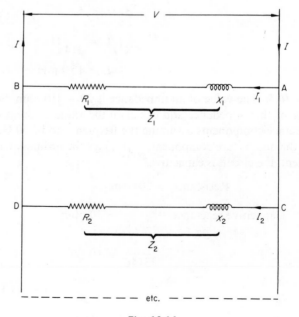

Fig. 10.14

Voltage drop from A to B = voltage drop from C to D = V

$$\therefore I_1 Z_1 = I_2 Z_2 = V$$

$$\therefore I_1 = \frac{V}{Z_1} \quad \text{and} \quad I_2 = \frac{V}{Z_2}$$

If the resultant current is I and the equivalent impedance is Z, then,

$$I = I_1 + I_2 + \cdots$$

$$\therefore \frac{V}{Z} = \frac{V}{Z_1} + \frac{V}{Z_2} + \cdots$$

$$\therefore \frac{1}{Z} = \frac{1}{Z_1} + \frac{1}{Z_2} + \cdots \tag{10.4}$$

It is convenient to denote the reciprocals in (10.4) by new symbols, descriptions and units.

$$\frac{1}{Z} = Y = \text{admittance in siemens}$$

Hence, if admittances are connected in parallel, then

$$Y = Y_1 + Y_2 + \cdots$$

Susceptance

The impedance due to an inductive reactance is given by,

$$Z_L = R + jX_L$$

$$\therefore \text{Admittance} = \frac{1}{Z_L} = Y_L = \frac{1}{R + jX_L}$$

$$= \frac{(R - jX_L)}{(R + jX_L)(R - jX_L)}$$

$$= \frac{R - jX_L}{R^2 + X_L^2}$$

$$\therefore Y_L = \frac{R}{R^2 + X_L^2} - \frac{jX_L}{R^2 + X_L^2} \tag{10.5}$$

Hence the admittance, Y_L, is a complex number, the ordinary component, $R/(R^2 + X_L^2)$, being the conductance G_L, and the quadrature component, $X_L/(R^2 + X_L^2)$, being termed the 'susceptance' and denoted by B_L.

$$\therefore Y_L = G_L - jB_L \tag{10.6}$$

Similarly, if we assume a capacitive reactance,

$$Z_C = R - jX_C$$
$$\therefore \ Y_C = G_C + jB_C$$

where G and B have the same form as in (10.5). It can now be seen that the impedance triangle of vectors has a counterpart, the admittance triangle of vectors.

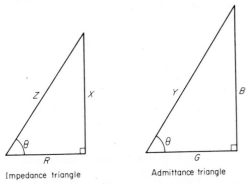

| Impedance triangle | Admittance triangle |

Fig. 10.15

Example 10.6. A circuit has an impedance of $10 + j4$ ohm at a frequency of 50 Hz.

(a) State the character of the reactance.
(b) Calculate the amplitude and phase angle of the impedance.
(c) Calculate the values of the resistance and the reactive component.
(d) Find the symbolic expression for the admittance of the circuit.
(e) Compare the impedance and admittance triangles.

(a) Since the reactive or quadrature component is positive, the circuit has an inductive reactance.
(b) Amplitude $= \sqrt{(10^2 + 4^2)} = 10 \cdot 8$ ohm
   Phase angle $\theta = \tan^{-1}(4/10) = 21° \ 48'$ leading
(c) The resistance is the ordinary component, 10 ohm.
   The reactive component $X_L = 2\pi f L = 4$ ohm.

$$\therefore \ L = \frac{4}{2 \times 3 \cdot 14 \times 50}$$
$$= \frac{4}{314}$$
$$= 0 \cdot 0128 \text{ H}$$

(d)
$$\text{Admittance } Y = \frac{1}{Z} = \frac{1}{10 + j4}$$

$$\therefore \ Y = \frac{(10 - j4)}{(10 + j4)(10 - j4)}$$

$$= \frac{10 - j4}{10^2 + 4^2}$$

$$= \frac{10}{116} - \frac{j4}{116}$$

$$= 0 \cdot 086 - j0 \cdot 0345 \text{ S}$$

$$\therefore \ \text{Amplitude } = \sqrt{(0 \cdot 086^2 + 0 \cdot 0345^2)} = 0 \cdot 0927$$

$$\therefore \ \text{Phase angle } = \theta = \tan^{-1}(-0 \cdot 0345/0 \cdot 086) = -0 \cdot 4$$

$$= -21° \ 48'$$

(e)

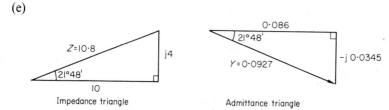

Impedance triangle   Admittance triangle

Fig. 10.16

Example 10.7. An inductance of 0·15 H and resistance 10 ohm is in parallel with a capacitance of 50 μF and resistance of 20 ohm. A voltage

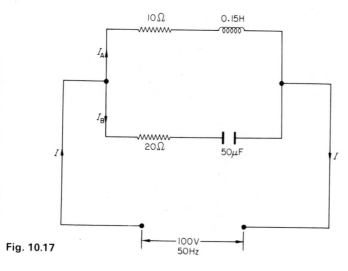

Fig. 10.17

of 100 V, frequency 50 Hz is applied to the circuit. Calculate the resultant current in the circuit and its phase relative to the supply voltage.

Branch A of circuit

$$Z_A = R + jX_L$$
$$= R + j2\pi fL$$
$$= 10 + j314(0 \cdot 15)$$
$$= 10 + j47 \cdot 1 \text{ ohm}$$

$$\therefore Y_A = \frac{1}{Z_A} = \frac{1}{10 + j47 \cdot 1}$$

$$\therefore Y_A = \frac{10 - j47 \cdot 1}{(10 + j47 \cdot 1)(10 - j47 \cdot 1)}$$

$$= \frac{10 - j47 \cdot 1}{10^2 + 47 \cdot 1^2}$$

$$= \frac{10}{10^2 + 47 \cdot 1^2} - \frac{j47 \cdot 1}{10^2 + 47 \cdot 1^2}$$

$$= \frac{10}{2319} - \frac{j47 \cdot 1}{2319}$$

$$= 0 \cdot 00432 - j0 \cdot 0203 \text{ S}$$

Branch B of circuit

$$Z_B = R - jX_C$$

$$= R - \frac{j}{2\pi fC}$$

$$= 20 - \frac{j}{314 \times 50 \times 10^{-6}}$$

$$= 20 - j63 \cdot 6 \text{ ohm}$$

$$\therefore Y_B = \frac{1}{Z_B} = \frac{1}{20 - j63 \cdot 6}$$

$$Y_B = \frac{20 + j63 \cdot 6}{(20 - j63 \cdot 6)(20 + j63 \cdot 6)}$$

$$= \frac{20 + j63 \cdot 6}{20^2 + 63 \cdot 6^2}$$

$$= \frac{20}{20^2 + 63\cdot6^2} + \frac{j63\cdot6}{20^2 + 63\cdot6^2}$$

$$= 0\cdot00450 + j0\cdot0143 \text{ S}$$

$$Y_{AB} = Y_A + Y_B$$

$$= 0\cdot00432 - j0\cdot0203 + 0\cdot00450 + j0\cdot0143$$

$$= 0\cdot00882 - j0\cdot0060 \text{ S}$$

$$\therefore Z_{AB} = \frac{1}{0\cdot00882 - j0\cdot0060}$$

$$= \frac{0\cdot00882 + j0\cdot0060}{(0\cdot00882 - j0\cdot0060)(0\cdot00882 + j0\cdot0060)}$$

$$= \frac{0\cdot00882 + j0\cdot0060}{0\cdot00882^2 + 0\cdot0060^2}$$

$$= \frac{0\cdot00882}{1\cdot138 \times 10^{-4}} + \frac{j0\cdot006}{1\cdot138 \times 10^{-4}}$$

$$= 77\cdot6 + j52\cdot8 \text{ ohm}$$

$$\therefore \text{ Amplitude of } Z_{AB}$$

$$= \sqrt{(77\cdot6^2 + 52\cdot8^2)}$$

$$= \sqrt{(6021 + 2787)}$$

$$= 93\cdot9 \text{ ohm}$$

$$\therefore I_{AB} = \frac{V}{Z_{AB}} = \frac{100}{93\cdot9} \text{ A}$$

$$= 1\cdot07 \text{ A}$$

$$\therefore \text{ Phase angle} = \theta = \tan^{-1}\left(\frac{52\cdot8}{77\cdot6}\right) = 34° 12'$$

Since the total impedance, Z_{AB}, is inductive, the supply current is lagging 34° 12' behind the supply voltage.

EXERCISE 10.1

1. Show each of the following complex numbers on an Argand diagram as a vector OP, indicating their real and imaginary components.

   (a) $2 + 3j$, (b) $-4 + j$, (c) $5 - 2j$, (d) $-3 - 4j$

2. Find the sum of $3 + 2j$ and $4 + 3j$, (a) algebraically, (b) vectorially on an Argand diagram.

3. Represent $5 + 2j$ as a vector on an Argand diagram and show the result of rotating it through $90°$ in an anti-clockwise direction. Verify your result by comparing it with the result of multiplying $5 + 2j$ by j.

4. Evaluate the following products, giving answers in the form $a + jb$.

   (a) $(2 - 3j)(1 + j)$ (b) $(-3 + 2j)(4 - 4j)$

   (c) $(3 + 5j)^2$ (d) $(-1 - j)(-1 + j)$

5. Simplify the following, by rationalizing the denominators; give answers in the form $a + jb$.

   (a) $\dfrac{2 + 3j}{4 - 2j}$ (b) $\dfrac{1 - 4j}{5 + 3j}$

   (c) $\dfrac{6 - 3j}{6 + 3j}$ (d) $\dfrac{-2 - 5j}{-1 - 4j}$

6. Solve the equation $2x^2 - 4x + 5 = 0$, giving the solutions in the form $a + jb$.

7. Find the magnitude and direction of the resultant of the addition of the pairs of vectors represented by the following complex numbers.

   (a) $4 + 5j$ and $2 + 7j$

   (b) $3 - 2j$ and $1 + j$

   (c) $-2 + 4j$ and $-3 + 2j$

   (d) $-3 - 5j$ and $-1 - 6j$

8. Express $\dfrac{1 + 2j}{2 + 5j} + \dfrac{3 - j}{4 - 2j}$ as one complex number in the form $a + jb$.

9. Express the impedance Z of an a.c. circuit containing resistance R and inductance L in series, as a complex number.

10. Find the resultant impedance in complex number form of three impedances in series whose values are, $1 + j4$, $3 + j5$, and $2 - j$. From this resultant state the magnitude and phase angle.

11. The value of an impedance is $20 - j10$ ohm. State whether this is inductive or capacitive and find the resistance and inductance (or capacitance) assuming the frequency to be 50 Hz.

12. Express in complex number form, the impedance of an inductance of 0·8 H in series with a resistance of 500 ohm; assume frequency to be 800 Hz. State the magnitude and phase angle of the impedance.

13. Express in complex number form, the impedance of a capacitance of 3 μF in series with a resistance of 40 ohm; assume frequency to be 1000 Hz. State the magnitude of the impedance and its phase angle.

14. A sinusoidal voltage of r.m.s. value 50 V and frequency 100 Hz is applied across a circuit containing an inductor of 1·5 H in series with a capacitor of 10 μF and a resistor of 100 ohm. Calculate the current flowing in the form $a + jb$, and represent the result on an Argand diagram.

15. An inductance of 0·2 H and resistance 20 ohm is in parallel with a second inductance of 0·3 H and resistance 50 ohm. Assuming a frequency of 50 Hz, represent these impedances by complex numbers and find their resultant.

16. Calculate the admittance of a circuit containing an inductance of 15 μH in series with a resistance of 40 ohm, assuming frequency to be 200 kHz.

17. Calculate the admittance of a circuit containing a capacitance of 30 pF in series with a resistance of 60 ohm, assuming frequency to be 50 MHz.

18. Find the resultant impedance of the circuit shown in Fig. 10.18, assuming frequency to be 100 kHz.

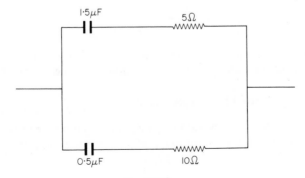

Fig. 10.18

19. In the circuit shown in Fig. 10.19, calculate the resultant impedance, assuming frequency to be 1 MHz.

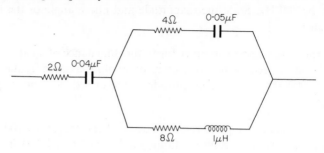

Fig. 10.19

20. Impedances Z_1 and Z_2 are connected in parallel. Express their combined impedance in the form $a + jb$, given that $Z_1 = 4 - j3$ and $Z_2 = 5 + j2$.

C.G.L.I. T.T. (part Qn.)

21. If $z = \dfrac{\sqrt{3} + j}{1 - j}$, express z in the form $a + jb$, and prove that the argument (angle) of z is $5\pi/12$ radian.

C.G.L.I. T.T. (part Qn.)

22. Express in complex number form the impedance in ohms of a choke of inductance 3 mH and a series resistance of 4 ohms at a frequency of 800 Hz.

Also obtain the phase relation between the current through the choke and the 800 Hz alternating voltage applied across it.

C.G.L.I. T.T. (part Qn.)

23. The characteristic impedance of a transmission line, Z_0, is given by,

$$Z_0 = \sqrt{\dfrac{R + j\omega L}{G + j\omega C}}$$

For distortionless transmission, the imaginary component of Z_0 must be zero. Show that this condition is obtained when $LG = RC$.

10.12 Polar form of a complex number

The vector OP, or the position of the point P, has been expressed in the cartesian form $a + jb$. It is often useful to use the polar form of expression, $r|\underline{\theta}$, where $a = r \cos \theta$ and $b = r \sin \theta$. Hence

$$a + jb = r \cos \theta + jr \sin \theta = r(\cos \theta + j \sin \theta)$$

The amplitude r is called the modulus, and θ the argument, of the complex number.

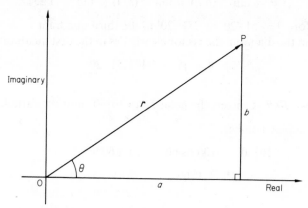

Fig. 10.20

It follows that

$$r = \sqrt{(a^2 + b^2)} \quad \text{and} \quad \theta = \tan^{-1}(b/a)$$

In converting from the cartesian form to polar form, it is advisable to identify, by diagram, the quadrant in which the vector lies, since the solution of $\tan \theta = b/a$ lies in either of two quadrants.

Example 10.8. Convert the complex number $4 + 5j$ into the equivalent polar form

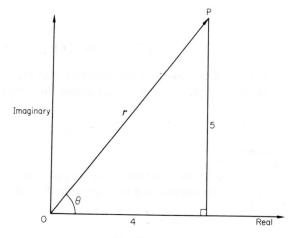

Fig. 10.21

$$r = \sqrt{(a^2 + b^2)} = \sqrt{(4^2 + 5^2)} = \sqrt{41} = 6\cdot403$$

$$\theta = \tan^{-1}(b/a) = \tan^{-1}(5/4) = \tan^{-1}(1\cdot25)$$

Therefore $\theta = 51° \ 20'$ or $231° \ 20'$ in the third quadrant.

From the diagram, the vector clearly lies in the first quadrant: hence

$$4 + j5 = 6\cdot403\underline{|51° \ 20'}$$

Example 10.9. Convert the polar form $10\underline{|60°}$ into the cartesian form of a complex number.

$$10\underline{|60°} = 10(\cos 60° + j \sin 60°)$$
$$= 5 + j5\sqrt{3}$$

10.13 Multiplication

Let $r_1\underline{|\theta_1}$ and $r_2\underline{|\theta_2}$ represent any two complex numbers in polar form.

$$r_1\underline{|\theta_1} \times r_2\underline{|\theta_2} = r_1(\cos \theta_1 + j \sin \theta_1) \times r_2(\cos \theta_2 + j \sin \theta_2)$$

$$= r_1 r_2 [(\cos \theta_1 \cos \theta_2 - \sin \theta_1 \sin \theta_2)$$
$$+ j(\sin \theta_1 \cos \theta_2 + \cos \theta_1 \sin \theta_2)]$$
$$= r_1 r_2 [\cos(\theta_1 + \theta_2) + j \sin(\theta_1 + \theta_2)]$$
$$= r_1 r_2 \underline{|\theta_1 + \theta_2}$$

Hence

$$r_1\underline{|\theta_1} \times r_2\underline{|\theta_2} = r_1 r_2 \underline{|\theta_1 + \theta_2}$$

The multiplication of two complex numbers in polar form is achieved by *multiplying* their moduli r_1 and r_2 and *adding* their arguments, θ_1 and θ_2.

10.14 Division

Since division is a converse process, it can be performed by *dividing* the moduli r_1 and r_2 and subtracting the arguments θ_1 and θ_2. Hence

$$\frac{r_1\underline{|\theta_1}}{r_2\underline{|\theta_2}} = \frac{r_1}{r_2}\underline{|\theta_1 - \theta_2}$$

Example 10.10. Multiply $(3 + j4)$ by $(2 + j3)$, (a) in cartesian form, (b) in polar form, and compare the results in polar form.

(a)
$$(3 + j4)(2 + j3) = 6 - 12 + j17$$
$$= -6 + j17$$

Hence
$$\text{Modulus } r = \sqrt{(6^2 + 17^2)} = \sqrt{325} = 18\cdot03$$
$$\text{Argument } \theta = \tan^{-1}(17/-6) = \tan^{-1} - 2\cdot8333$$

The complex number, $-6 + j17$, is in the second quadrant, hence $\theta = 109° 26'$

(b)
$$3 + j4 = 5\lfloor\tan^{-1} 1\cdot3333 = 5\lfloor53° 8'$$

$$2 + j3 = \sqrt{13}\lfloor\tan^{-1} 1\cdot5 = \sqrt{13}\lfloor56° 19'$$

$$\therefore (3 + j4)(2 + j3) = 5\lfloor53° 8' \times \sqrt{13}\lfloor56° 19'$$

$$= 5\sqrt{13}\lfloor53° 8' + 56° 19'$$

$$= 5 \times 3\cdot606\lfloor109° 27'$$

$$= 18\cdot03\lfloor109° 27'$$

Hence the modulus, 18·03, and the argument, 109° 27', compare favourably with those obtained in (a).

Example 10.11. Divide $5 + j12$ by $3 - j4$, (a) in cartesian form, by rationalizing the denominator, and (b) in polar form, and compare the results in cartesian form.

(a)
$$\frac{5 + j12}{3 - j4} = \frac{(5 + j12)(3 + j4)}{(3 - j4)(3 + j4)}$$

$$= \frac{15 - 48 + j56}{3^2 + 4^2}$$

$$= \frac{-33 + j56}{25}$$

$$= -\frac{33}{25} + \frac{j56}{25}$$

$$= -1\cdot32 + j2\cdot24 \tag{10.7}$$

(b)
$$5 + j12 = \sqrt{(5^2 + 12^2)}\ \lfloor\tan^{-1}(12/5)$$

$$= 13\lfloor 67°\ 23'$$

$$3 - j4 = \sqrt{(3^2 + 4^2)}\ \lfloor\tan^{-1}(-4/3)$$

$$= 5\lfloor -53°\ 8'$$

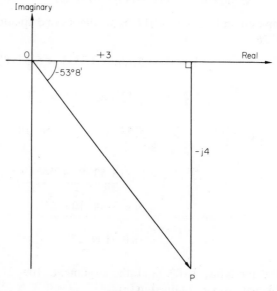

Fig. 10.22

Figure 10.22 indicates the correct quadrant for the argument, $-53°\ 8'$.

$$\therefore\ \frac{5 + j12}{3 - j4} = \frac{13\lfloor 67°\ 23'}{5\lfloor -53°\ 8'}$$

$$= 2·6\lfloor 67°\ 23' - (-53°\ 8')$$

$$= 2·6\lfloor 120°\ 31'$$

$$= 2·6\ (\cos 120°\ 31' + j\sin 120°\ 31')$$

$$= 2·6(-0·5077 + j0·8614)$$

$$= -1·32 + j2·24 \qquad\qquad (10.8)$$

Comparison of results (10.7) and (10.8) shows very close agreement.

10.15 Squares and square roots of complex numbers

From section 10.13,

$$r\underline{|\theta} \times r\underline{|\theta} = r^2\underline{|2\theta}$$

(a) The square of a complex number is produced by squaring the modulus r and doubling the argument θ.

(b) Conversely, a square root of a complex number can be found by taking the square root of the modulus and halving the argument. A real number has two square roots, equal in size, opposite in sign; a similar situation must be allowed for with complex numbers.

Example 10.12. Square the number $6 - j8$, (a) in cartesian form, and (b) in polar form, and compare results in cartesian form.

(a) $\qquad\qquad (6 - j8)(6 - j8) = 36 - 64 - j96$

$$= -28 - j96 \qquad\qquad (10.9)$$

(b) $\qquad\quad 6 - j8 = 10\underline{|\tan^{-1}(-8/6)} = 10\underline{|-53°\ 8'}$

$$= 10\underline{|306\ 52'}$$

$$\therefore\ (6 - j8)^2 = \left[10\underline{|306°\ 52'}\right]^2$$

$$= 100\underline{|613°\ 44'}$$

$$= 100\underline{|253°\ 44'}$$

$$= 100(\cos 253°\ 44' + j\sin 253°\ 44')$$

$$= 100(-\cos 73°\ 44' - j\sin 73°\ 44')$$

$$= 100(-0{\cdot}2801 - j0{\cdot}9600)$$

$$= -28{\cdot}01 - j96 \qquad\qquad (10.10)$$

Compare results (10.9) and (10.10).

Example 10.13. Find the two square roots of $6 + j8$, (a) in polar form, (b) in cartesian form, and (c) verify the result in cartesian form.

(a) Polar form

The modulus of $6 + j8 = \sqrt{(6^2 + 8^2)} = 10$

The argument of $6 + j8 = \theta = \tan^{-1}(8/6)$

$$= 53°\ 8'\ \text{or}\ 233°\ 8'$$

It is essential, in all statements of the form, $\theta = \tan^{-1}(b/a)$, to identify the quadrant of the Argand diagram which contains the given vector; this determines the correct value of θ. Since $6 + j8$ is in the first quadrant, $\theta = 53° 8'$ (Fig. 10.23).

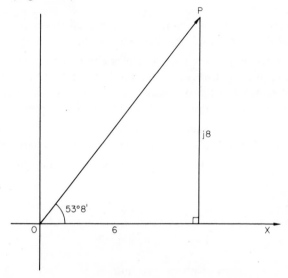

Fig. 10.23

There still remains a second ambiguity, which is the reason for the existence of two values of the square root. The position OP can be reached by an anti-clockwise rotation of $+53° 8'$ from OX or a clockwise rotation of $-306° 52'$ from OX (Fig. 10.24).

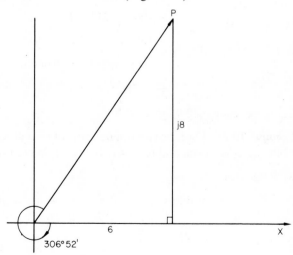

Fig. 10.24

Hence

$$6 + j8 = 10\underline{|53° \ 8'} \qquad \text{or} \qquad 10\underline{|-306° \ 52'}$$

$$\therefore \ \sqrt{(6 + j8)} = \sqrt{10}\underline{|26° \ 34'} \qquad \text{or} \qquad \sqrt{10}\underline{|-153° \ 26'}$$

$$= \sqrt{10}\underline{|26° \ 34'} \qquad \text{or} \qquad \sqrt{10}\underline{|206° \ 34'}$$

It should be noted that the two angles differ by 180° or π radians, which gives the two vectors a similar aspect to the equal and opposite values of the square roots of a real number (cf. $\sqrt{9} = \pm 3$). It is useful to represent a complex number by a single letter z, from which we write $|z|$ to represent the modulus.

Hence, if $z = a + jb$, one square root is $|z|^{1/2}\underline{|\tfrac{1}{2} \arg z}$ and the other is $|z|^{1/2}\underline{|\tfrac{1}{2} \arg z + \pi}$

(b) Cartesian form

From (a), $\sqrt{10}\underline{|26° \ 34'}$ is one square root of $6 + j8$.

$$\therefore \ \sqrt{(6 + j8)} = \sqrt{10}\underline{|26° \ 34'}$$

$$= \sqrt{10} \ (\cos 26° \ 34' + j \sin 26° \ 34')$$

$$= 3 \cdot 162(0 \cdot 8944 + j0 \cdot 4472)$$

$$= 2 \cdot 828 + j1 \cdot 414$$

(c) The result of (b) is verified if,

$$(2 \cdot 828 + j1 \cdot 414)^2 = 6 + j8$$

It is convenient to note that $2 \cdot 828 = 2\sqrt{2}$ and $1 \cdot 414 = \sqrt{2}$ approx.

$$\therefore \ (2 \cdot 828 + j1 \cdot 414)^2 = (2\sqrt{2} + j\sqrt{2})^2$$

$$= 8 + j^2 2 + 2(2\sqrt{2} \times j\sqrt{2})$$

$$= 8 - 2 + j8$$

$$= 6 + j8$$

It is left as an exercise for the student to verify in a similar manner the alternative value of the square root, $\sqrt{10}\underline{|206° \ 34'}$

EXERCISE 10.2

1. Express the following cartesian forms of complex numbers in polar form.

   (a) $2 + j4$ (b) $-4 + j3$

   (c) $6 - j8$ (d) $-8 - j5$

2. Express the following polar forms of complex numbers in cartesian form.

   (a) $10\underline{|50°}$ (b) $8\underline{|130°}$

   (c) $4\underline{|220°}$ (d) $6\underline{|318°}$

3. Multiply $(5 + j8)$ by $(2 + j6)$, (a) in cartesian form, (b) in polar form, and (c) verify the result in cartesian form.

4. Multiply $5\underline{|20°}$ by $9\underline{|100°}$, (a) in polar form, (b) in cartesian form, and (c) verify the result in polar form.

5. Divide $(10 - j5)$ by $(7 + j3)$ in polar form.

6. If $z = 2\underline{|42°}$, write down the values of (a) z^2 and (b) $\sqrt{z}$.

7. Express in the form $a + jb$,

   (a) $(2 + j3)^2 - j(1 - j9)$

   (b) $\dfrac{3 - j4}{1 + j2}$

   Express (b) also in the form $r\underline{|\theta}$. If this number be denoted by z, show on a sketch diagram the complex numbers z, $2jz$, z^2.

   CG.L.I. T.T.

8. If $z = 3 - j2$, express $1/z$, z^2 in the polar form $r\underline{|\theta}$.

   C.G.L.I. T.T. (part Qn.)

9. Prove that the impedance $Z_0 = \sqrt{\{(R + j\omega L)/(G + j\omega C)\}}$ is purely resistive (i.e., wholly real) when $RC = GL$. Calculate Z_0

either in cartesian *or* in polar form when $R = 22$, $L = 4 \times 10^{-3}$, $C = 0.008 \times 10^{-6}$, $\omega = 10^4$, and G is so small as to be negligible.

C.G.L.I. T.T. (part Qn.)

10. (a) Express $\dfrac{(1 + j2)^2}{1 - j}$ in the form $a + jb$

(b) Express $R + j\omega L$, $G + j\omega C$ in polar form as $r_1 \lfloor \theta_1$ and $r_2 \lfloor \theta_2$

respectively, and hence express

$$Z_0 = \sqrt{\{(R + j\omega L)/(G + j\omega C)\}}$$

in polar form. Show that Z_0 is real if $LG = RC$.

C.G.L.I. T.T.

11. (a) If $z = r(\cos \theta + j \sin \theta) = r\lfloor \theta$, prove

$$z_1 z_2 = r_1 r_2 \lfloor \theta_1 + \theta_2$$

(b) Express $(1 - j\frac{1}{3})/(1 + j)$ in both polar and cartesian forms as a single complex number.

(c) Obtain the two square roots of the complex number $-4 + j3$ in the form $a + jb$.

C.G.L.I. T.T.

12. (a) Explain with the aid of a diagram how a vector in a plane can be represented by a complex number in the form $a + jb$. Show that the sum of two such complex numbers can represent the resultant of two co-planar vectors.

(b) If $z = -5 + j12$,

(i) Express $\dfrac{1}{z} + \dfrac{1}{z + 14}$ in the form $a + jb$.

(ii) Express z and z^2 in the polar form $r \lfloor \theta$.

C.G.L.I. T.T.

13. The in-phase and quadrature, leading, components of the current taken by an a.c. circuit from a 250 V supply are 40 A and 20 A respectively.

Calculate, (a) conductance, (b) susceptance, (c) admittance, (d) the character and magnitude of the reactive component, assuming frequency to be 50 Hz.

16

14. Figure 10.25 shows two circuits which are equivalent. Calculate the conductance and susceptance of the capacitive branch of the parallel circuit.

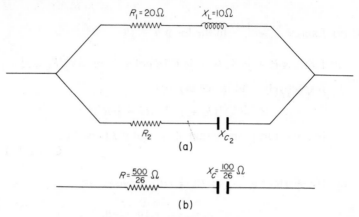

Fig. 10.25

Answers to Exercises

EXERCISE 1.1

1. (a) -5; (b) 0.4; (e) $a - b$; (f) 1; (h) 2
2. (a) -92, 8.8, $21a - 20b$, $(p + 19q)/q$ and 40
   (b) -294, 40.8, $90a - 78b$, $(12p + 66q)/q$ and 156
3. $20, 22\frac{1}{2}, 25, 27\frac{1}{2}, \ldots$
4. $-14, -24, -34, -44, -54$
5. $-24, -16, -8, 0, \ldots$
6. $1, 2\frac{1}{2}, 4, 5\frac{1}{2}, \ldots$
7. 27th
8. $m(b - a)$ or $m(d - b)$
9. 1729 m
10. 17.2 km

EXERCISE 1.2

1. (b), (c), (d), (e), (f), and (g)
2. (a) $49,152$; $\frac{1}{256}$; $390,625$; $(b/a)^{13}$; -1; $-\frac{4}{625}$
   (b) $65,535$; $\frac{255}{256}$; $325,520$; $\dfrac{(a^8 + b^8)(a^4 + b^4)(a^2 + b^2)}{ba^{13}}$; 0; $\frac{260416}{625}$
3. $4\frac{1}{2}$
4. 6, 12, 24, 48, 96
5. $100, 200, 400, \ldots$
6. 574, 302, 158, 83, 44, 23, rev/min
   10, 19, 36, 69, 130, 250 mm
7. 1st series; G.P.; log (series); A.P., $d = 0.3010$
8. $0.5, 0.612, 0.748, 0.915, 1.12, 1.37, 1.68, 2.05, 2.5\ \Omega$

9. (a) 15 yr (16th G.P. term)

(b) $r < 1 : 7 \cdot 4\dot{5} = 7 + \dfrac{45}{10^2} + \dfrac{45}{10^4} + \dfrac{45}{10^6} + \cdots; \frac{82}{11}$

10. 6100; 12 yr

11. 486 m; 1290 turns; 0·062 mm; 9 rad/sec; 1·8 rad/sec

EXERCISE 1.3

1. $1 + t/2 - t^2/8 + t^3/16 - \cdots$

2. $1 + 4y + 12y^2 + 32y^3 + \cdots$

3. $15x^4/16$

4. $-32x^5$

5. $2[1 + 3x/8 - 9x^2/128 + 27x^3/1024 - \cdots]$

6. $\frac{1}{3}[1 + x/6 + x^2/24 + 5x^3/432 + \cdots]$

7. 10·3923

8. 1·414214

9. $(1 + x/2); (1 + x/2); (1 + x)$

10. $\frac{1}{8}[1 - x/24 + 431x^2/576 - \cdots]$

11. $g = 4\pi^2 l/T^2; \pm 0.8\%$

12. (a) $1 - x/2 - x^2/8 - x^3/16 - 5x^4/128 - \cdots$

Coefficient of $x^r = \dfrac{-1 \cdot 3 \cdot 5 \cdots (2r - 3)}{2^r/r!}$

$-1 < x < 1; \ 1 \cdot 732$

13. (a) $1 - x/2 + 3x^2/8 - 5x^3/16 + \cdots; -1 < x < 1$

$r\text{th term} = \dfrac{1 \cdot 3 \cdot 5 \cdots (2r - 3)x^{r-1}(-1)^{r-1}}{2^{r-1}(r - 1)!}$

(b) 0° C (actual, 0·4° C)

14. $\pm 0.5\%$

EXERCISE 2.1

1. (a) 3·935   (b) 0·03175   (c) 0·4585
   (d) 1·751   (e) 1·0149   (f) 3·8245
   (g) $\bar{5}$·1102   (h) 6·9078   (i) 2·1320
   (j) 6·5196   (k) $\bar{2}$·6972   (l) $\bar{5}$·3948

2. (a) 5·794   (b) 20·27   (c) 0·4668
   (d) 0·03708   (e) 1144   (f) 0·1832
   (g) 220·2   (h) 0·3679

3. (a) 2·5543   (b) 1·0098   (c) 1·9095
   (d) 0·4621   (e) 0·3466   (f) 3·2260
   (g) 3·1372   (h) 0·3017

4. $T_1 = 65 \cdot 0; \theta = 0 \cdot 719$ rad

5. 7·35 A   **6.** 0·0313   **7.** 6·73 pF

8. 0·026 H   **9.** 0·823   **10.** 50

11. (a) 4·6052   (b) 3·9120   (c) 0·02744 m

12. (a) $2·566 \times 10^{-3}$ (b) 0·6059

13. 4·55   **14.** 2·3   **15.** (b) 16·1

16. (a) (i) 2·079; (ii) 1·145   (b) 6·77

17. 10·2   **18.** 61·2; $\mu = \dfrac{1}{\theta \sec \alpha} \log \left(\dfrac{T_1}{T_2} \right)$

19. Area = 0·408; mean value = 0·26

20. $v = V(1 - e^{-t/CR})$; $R = 10^4 \, \Omega$

    (a) 10 mA   (b) 3·68 mA   (c) zero

21. $i = 0·25(1 - e^{-40t})$

    (a) zero   (b) 0·25 A; $t = 0$

22. Straight line, $v = 100t$; $v = 100(1 - e^{-t/10})$; $T = 10$ sec
    (a) 0·1 mA   (b) zero

EXERCISE 2.2

1. $I_m = 26·1$; $k = -0·005$ **2.** $T_0 = 10$; $\mu = 0·5$

3. $T = T_0 e^{-kt}$ where $T_0 = 490$, $k = 0·02$; (a) 387; (b) 387

4. $k = 0·2$

5. $P_0 = 30·3$; $k = -3·56 \times 10^{-5}$

6. $\log V_0 = 1·61$; $V_0 = 5$V; $t = 2·31$ min

7. $R/L = 101$; $T = 0·0099$ sec

8. $a = 3·2$; $k = 0·0308$; 1790 to 1860

9. $a = 37$; $k = 0·56$

10. $a = 7·0$; $k = 2·8$

EXERCISE 2.3

1. $\mu = \dfrac{1}{\theta} \log (T_1/T_2)$ **2.** $b = T \log \left(\dfrac{AT^2}{I} \right)$

3. $d = r(e^{k/C} + 1)$ **4.** $d_2 = d_1 \, e^{L/k}$

5. $t = \dfrac{1}{k} \log \left(\dfrac{A}{q} \right)$ **6.** $C = \dfrac{t}{R \log (E/Ri)}$

7. $T = \dfrac{t}{\log [\theta_f/(\theta_f - \theta)]}$ **8.** $V_1 = V_2 \, e^{-G}$

9. $t = CR \log \left(\dfrac{V}{V - v} \right)$ **10.** $d_1 = d_2 \, (e^{0·4343t/CR})$

11. $a = b \, e^{-kl/2C}$ **12.** $n = \dfrac{\log P_1 - \log P_2}{\log V_2 - \log V_1}$

13. $v = \left(\dfrac{2gdh}{kl}\right)^{1/n}$

14. (a) $1 \cdot 585$;   (b) $h = \dfrac{d}{2}\,(e^{M/k} - 1)^{1/2}$

15. $i \simeq \dfrac{Et}{L}$; $i \simeq \dfrac{Et}{L}\left(1 - \dfrac{Rt}{2L}\right)$ $L = \dfrac{Rt}{\log\left(\dfrac{E}{E - Ri}\right)}$

16. $h = \dfrac{1}{2k}\log\left(\dfrac{u^2 k + g}{g}\right)$; $u^2 \simeq 2gh(1 + kh)$

17. $\theta_h = \theta_0\,e^{-h/a}$; $67 \cdot 0$ cm

EXERCISE 3.1

1. $5x^4$

2. $-2x$

3. $1 - 4x$

4. $6(3x + 1)$

5. $\dfrac{4x^{1/3}}{3}$

6. $6t^2 - 2t + 3$

7. $-\dfrac{4}{q^3}$

8. $-\dfrac{1}{v^2}$

9. $-\dfrac{20}{r^3}$

10. $4\pi R^2$

11. $2 + 2x$

12. $\dfrac{1}{x^{1/2}} - \dfrac{3x^{1/2}}{2}$

13. $-\dfrac{1}{3x^{4/3}}$

14. $-\dfrac{3}{2x^{3/2}} + \dfrac{1}{x^2}$

15. $-\dfrac{6}{x^3}$

16. anx^{n-1}

17. $-\dfrac{ak}{x^{a+1}}$

18. $2ax + b$

19. $-\dfrac{a}{x^2} - b$

20. $2ax^{2a-1} + bx^{b-1}$

21. 9

22. $-\dfrac{1}{54}$

23. 3

24. 0

25. 3

26. $5(x^2 + 3x)^4(2x + 3)$

27. $\dfrac{2}{(1 + 4x)^{1/2}}$

28. $\dfrac{6}{(1 - x)^7}$

29. $-\dfrac{(3x - 4)}{2x^2(x - 2)^{3/2}}$

30. $x\,e^{3x}(3x + 2)$

31. $\dfrac{3x - 1}{x} + 3\log x$

32. $e^x\left(\dfrac{1}{x} + \log x\right)$

33. $e^{2x+1}(2x + 5)$

34. $\dfrac{1 - x}{2\,e^{x/2}x^{1/2}}$

35. $\dfrac{x(2 - 3x)}{e^{3x}}$

36. $\dfrac{2}{3(2x + 1)} - \dfrac{\log (2x + 1)}{3x^2}$

37. $-\dfrac{(3x + 10)}{x^3}$

38. $\dfrac{2}{(1 - x)^2}$

39. $-\dfrac{1}{x}$

40. $6e^{2x} + 6e^{3x}$

41. $5;\ -2$

42. (a) 25 A/sec; (b) 15·2 A/sec

43. (a) 500 V/sec; (b) 358 V/sec

EXERCISE 3.2

1. (a) $100 \cos 100t$ (b) $-3\omega \sin \omega t$
    (c) $100 \cos (50t - \pi)$ (d) $-\pi f \sin (2\pi ft + \pi/2)$
    (e) $20I_m \cos (20t - 0{\cdot}2)$ (f) $-V_m \sin \theta + 2IR \cos 2\theta$

2. (a) $e^{2t} (\cos t + 2 \sin t)$
    (b) $2 \cos 2\theta \cos 3\theta - 3 \sin 2\theta \sin 3\theta$
    (c) $-e^{-t} (\cos t + \sin t)$
    (d) $e^{2\theta} [2 \sin (3\theta - \pi/3) + 3 \cos (3\theta - \pi/3)]$
    (e) $(1/x) \cos x - \log 3x \sin x$
    (f) $\omega\, e^{\omega t}(2 \cos 2\omega t + \sin 2\omega t)$

3. (a) $\dfrac{1}{\cos \theta - 1}$ (b) $\dfrac{e^x (\sin x - \cos x)}{\sin^2 x}$

    (c) $-\operatorname{cosec}^2 \theta$ (d) $\dfrac{2(\cos 2t - \sin 2t)}{e^{-2t}}$

    (e) $-\omega \operatorname{cosec}^2 \omega t$

    (f) $\dfrac{2 \cos (10t - 0{\cdot}2) + 20t \sin (10t - 0{\cdot}2)}{\cos^2 (10t - 0{\cdot}2)}$

4. $\frac{1}{2}$ **5.** -5000π A/sec   **6.** 247 V/sec

7. 26° 34′   **8.** 0·00469 sec   **9.** 0·0268 sec

10. $\dfrac{\pi}{4}$ to $\dfrac{5\pi}{4}$ **11.** $\theta = 97°\ 15';\ y = -0{\cdot}968$

EXERCISE 4.1

1. Min $(1, -1)$ **2.** Max $(\frac{1}{2}, 12\frac{1}{4})$

3. Max $(2, 30)$; Min $(3, 29)$ **4.** Min $(4, 6)$

5. Max $(-\frac{1}{2}, -4)$; Min $(\frac{1}{2}, 4)$ **6.** Max $(1, 8)$; Min $(-3, -24)$

7. Min $(1, -4/3)$ **8.** Min $(9, -1)$

9. 4 ? 2   **10.** Max 19; Min -13

11. $a = 6; b = 5; c = 4$ **12.** (a) $\frac{2}{3}$, 2 sec; (b) $-4, +4$ m/sec^2

13. (a) 100 m/sec; (b) $3\frac{1}{6}$ sec; (c) $156\frac{1}{4}$ m; (d) 100 m/sec

14. 2; 5   **15.** Max $42\frac{5}{8}$; Min $-13\cdot7$

16. 3   **17.** 9

18. $0\cdot644$ **19.** Max $(-2, 0\cdot541)$; Min $(0, 0)$

21. 216 cm^2 **22.** $r = 5\sqrt{6}/3$ cm; $h = 10\sqrt{6}/3$ cm

23. (a) $2x - 16/x^2$; (b) $-Cv_0\omega \sin \omega t$; $Cv_0\omega$

24. $3 \cos 3\theta$ **25.** $-8 \sin 4\theta$

26. $10^4 \cos 100t$ **27.** $10^4 \cos 200t$

28. $2\pi f I_m \cos 2\pi ft$ **29.** 284 V/sec

30. -8330 A/sec   **31.** $-0\cdot2080$ A

32. $-57\cdot3$ mV   **33.** (b) (i) 279 V/sec; (ii) 34·9 V/sec

34. (a) $10x + 7/x^2$
    (b) $4R \sin \omega t + 4\omega L \cos \omega t = v$; $v = 40 \sin 3000t + 60 \cos 3000t$

35. (a) $6x - 4/x^2$
    (b) $i = 0\cdot03 \sin 100\pi t$ A; $e = -0\cdot0096\pi \cos 100\pi t$ V
    Peak e.m.f. $= 0\cdot0096\pi = 0\cdot03014$ V

EXERCISE 5.1

(Questions 1 to 20 require addition of a constant)

1. $x - x^2 + x^3$ **2.** $4x^3 + \dfrac{5x^2}{2} - 2x$

3. $-\dfrac{1}{2x^2}$ **4.** $\dfrac{2x^{5/2}}{5}$

5. $\dfrac{x^4}{2} - x^3 + \dfrac{x^2}{2}$ **6.** $\dfrac{6x^{5/2}}{5} - \dfrac{2x^{7/2}}{7}$

7. $\dfrac{acx^3}{3} + \dfrac{(bc - ad)x^2}{2} - bdx$ **8.** $\dfrac{q}{2x^2} - \dfrac{p}{x}$

9. $\dfrac{\pi r^3}{3} - \pi r^2 h$ **10.** $2t^{1/2} + 2t^{-1}$

11. $\dfrac{x^{n+1}}{(n+1)^2}$ **12.** $\dfrac{nx^{(1+n)/n}}{(n+1)}$

13. $Ei - \dfrac{i^2R}{2}$ **14.** $\frac{1}{2}CV^2$

15. $\frac{1}{2}LI^2$ **16.** $\dfrac{x^2}{2} + 2x$

17. $\dfrac{4\pi}{3}\sqrt{\dfrac{l^3}{g}}$ **18.** $r^2x - \dfrac{x^3}{3}$

19. $\theta - \dfrac{\theta^2}{2} + \theta^3$ **20.** $\frac{1}{3}\pi h[R^2r + Rr + r^2]$

21. $y = \dfrac{3x^2}{2} - 2x + \dfrac{5}{2}$

22. $s = \dfrac{t^2}{2} - \dfrac{t^3}{3} + t + \dfrac{5}{3}$

23. $h = 6t^{1/2} + \dfrac{2t^{3/2}}{3} - \dfrac{49}{3}$

24. $v = t - \dfrac{t^3}{3} + \dfrac{11}{3}$

25. $i = \dfrac{6t^{5/2}}{5} + \dfrac{3t^2}{2} + \dfrac{4t^{3/2}}{3} + 2t - \dfrac{121}{30}$

26. $y = x^2 - \dfrac{x^3}{6} + \dfrac{x}{2} + \dfrac{5}{3}$

27. $s = \dfrac{t^5}{20} - \dfrac{t^4}{4} + 2t^2 - \dfrac{14t}{5} + 3$

28. $16\frac{1}{2}$

29. 16·7 m/sec

30. 34·1 m

31. (a) 12·8 km; (b) 4·512 km

32. -12

33. 61·3 m

34. 1·70 sec

EXERCISE 5.2

1. $-\frac{2}{3}$

2. $\frac{11}{6}$

3. 0

4. $-\frac{124}{15}$

5. $-1\frac{1}{3}$

6. $\frac{68}{3}$

7. 1·6

8. 6

9. $-\frac{2}{3}$

10. -6

11. (a) $2\frac{3}{4}$; (b) $2\frac{2}{3}$; (c) $2\frac{2}{3}$

12. (a) 24·4; (b) 24·2

13. (a) 0; (b) 2·21

14. $4\frac{1}{2}$

15. $1\frac{1}{3}$

EXERCISE 5.3

1. $\dfrac{e^{3x}}{3}$

2. $4e^{x/2}$

3. 2·35

4. $10\,e^{0·1x} + e^{x+a}$

5. $-5·72$

6. $\frac{1}{3} \log (3x - 2)$

7. $-0·6931$

8. 1·82

9. $x^2/2 + 3x + 2 \log (x + 2)$

10. $6x + 16 \log (x - 2)$

11. 6·389

12. 1·58

13. 0·5493

14. 0·3054

15. 1·649 C

16. $C \log (v_1/v_0)$

17. 0·658 V

18. $\frac{1}{2} LI^2$ J

EXERCISE 6.1

1. (a) $\sin \omega t \cos \alpha + \cos \omega t \sin \alpha$
(b) $\sin \theta \cos \beta - \cos \theta \sin \beta$
(c) $\cos 50t \cos \theta - \sin 50t \sin \theta$
(d) $\cos 2\pi ft \cos \alpha + \sin 2\pi ft \sin \alpha$

2. (a) $\dfrac{\sqrt{3}+1}{2\sqrt{2}}$; (b) $\dfrac{\sqrt{3}-1}{2\sqrt{2}}$ **3.** $\dfrac{\sqrt{3}-1}{2\sqrt{2}}$

4. (a) $\frac{24}{25}$; (b) $\frac{7}{25}$; (c) $\frac{24}{7}$ **5.** $\sqrt{2}-1$

10. $13\sin(\theta+\phi)$; $\phi=\tan^{-1}(12/5)$ **11.** $76°\,16'$; $316°\,16'$

12. $6\cdot40$ **13.** $0\cdot983$ rad

14. $17\cos(\theta+\phi)$; $\phi=\tan^{-1}(15/8)=61°\,56'$

15. $33\cdot5\sin(\omega t+\phi)$; $\phi=\tan^{-1}(2)=63°\,26'$

16. $0\cdot0109$ sec

17. (a) $\sin A\cos B-\cos A\sin B$; $\cos A\cos B-\sin A\sin B$
(b) $A=-0\cdot619$; $B=2\cdot45$

18. (b) $\tan A=\dfrac{2t}{1-t^2}$; (c) $306°\,52'$

19. $\sin A\cos B+\cos A\sin B$; $\sin A\cos B-\cos A\sin B$;
$\frac{1}{2}[\sin 2\pi(F+f)t+\sin 2\pi(F-f)t]$

20. (a) $2\cdot62$ m/sec; (b) $3\cdot14$ m/sec; $i=15\sqrt{3}\sin\omega t+15\cos\omega t$

21. (c) $-167°\,56'$, $-55°\,40'$

22. (b) $13\cos(\theta+247°\,23')$; (c) $72°\,22'$, $287°\,38'$

23. (b) $168°\,26'$, $348°\,26'$

24. $\cos A\cos B-\sin A\sin B$; $\sin A\cos B+\cos A\sin B$;
$28\sin\omega t-21\cos\omega t$

25. (a) $\sin 3A=3\sin A-4\sin^3 A$; (c) $\phi=55°\,36'$ or $-78°\,12'$

EXERCISE 6.2

1. (a) $-3\cos\theta$ (b) $2\sin\theta$
(c) $-\frac{1}{2}\cos 2\theta+\frac{1}{3}\sin 3\theta$ (d) $-\frac{1}{2}\cos(2\theta+\pi)$

(e) $\frac{3}{4}\sin\left(4\theta-\dfrac{\pi}{2}\right)$ (f) $-\dfrac{50}{\omega}\cos\omega t$

(g) $\dfrac{1}{5}\sin 50t$ (h) $-\dfrac{5}{2\pi f}\cos 2\pi ft$

(i) $\frac{1}{2}\left(t-\dfrac{1}{2\omega}\sin 2\omega t\right)$ (j) $\frac{1}{2}\left(t+\dfrac{1}{4\pi f}\sin 4\pi ft\right)$

2. (a) $\dfrac{3-\sqrt{3}}{2}$ (b) $-\dfrac{3}{4}$ (c) $-\dfrac{(1+\sqrt{2})}{3\sqrt{2}}$

(d) $\dfrac{\pi}{2\omega}$ (e) $\dfrac{\pi}{2\omega}$ (f) 0 (g) $0\cdot0431$

(h) $0\cdot0854$ (i) 0 (j) 0

3. $\dfrac{2I_m}{\pi}$ A   **4.** $\dfrac{V_m}{\sqrt{2}}$ V   **5.** $\sqrt{250}$ A

6. $\dfrac{8\sqrt{3}}{\pi}$ V   **7.** $0\cdot143$ C   **8.** 1 A

EXERCISE 7.1

1. $I_1 = 1 \cdot 5, I_2 = 2 \cdot 5, I_3 = 3$

2. $I_1 = 2 \cdot 93, I_2 = 3 \cdot 41, I_3 = 1 \cdot 22$

3. $x = 2, y = 3 \cdot 5, z = 4 \cdot 5$ **4.** $0 \cdot 785$

5. $x = 1, y = 2; x = 2, y = -2$ **6.** ± 2

7. $x = \frac{1}{4}$ or 9 **8.** $-0 \cdot 405$

9. Negative, $2 < x < 5$

10. (a) $\frac{5}{3}, \frac{2}{3}$; (b) $\frac{1}{3}, -\frac{2}{3}$; (c) $a/2b, 3c/2b$; (d) $0, -1$

11. $\pm 4\sqrt{2}$

12. (a) $2\frac{1}{2}$; (b) -4; (c) $14\frac{1}{4}$; (d) $22\frac{1}{4}$

13. (a) Min -12 at $x = 4$ (b) Min $3\frac{7}{8}$ at $x = -1\frac{3}{4}$
    (c) Max $6\frac{1}{4}$ at $x = -1\frac{1}{2}$ (d) Max $7\frac{1}{3}$ at $x = -\frac{2}{3}$

14. $t = T \log \left(\dfrac{\theta_m}{\theta_m - \theta} \right)$ **15.** $C = \dfrac{t}{R \log (V_0/v)}$

16. $r = R \, e^{-k/2C}$ **17.** $D = d \, e^{V/2 \cdot 5 x \tan \psi}$

18. $t = CR \log \left(\dfrac{CV}{CV - q} \right)$ **19.** $0 \cdot 4888$

20. $12 \cdot 3$ **21.** $0 \cdot 00106$

22. $24 \cdot 2$ **23.** $21 \cdot 4$

24. $\pm 1 \cdot 41$ **25.** $\dfrac{\sqrt{Nt}}{10}$

26. (a) $x = 5/6$ or -2; $y = 7/9$ or -3
    (b) $y = 3(x - 7/3)^2 + 5/3$; $x = 7/3$, $dy/dx = 0$

27. (a) 10; (b) $1 \cdot 59$; (c) (i) $10 \cdot 2$, (ii) $k = e^{-Gmn/20(n-1)}$

28. 61 mA

29. $b^2 - 4ac \geqslant 0$; a and c have same sign

30. (a) $a = 2, b = -12, c = 10$; (b) 9 or -25

31. (a) $5\frac{1}{2}, -4\frac{1}{2}$; (b) $x = 1\frac{1}{2}$ or 6, $y = -6$ or 3

32. (a) $3\,\Omega$ or $12\,\Omega$; (b) $x = 6$ or $-5 \cdot 2$, $y = -2$ or $3 \cdot 6$

33. $x = 3, y = \frac{2}{3}, z = -2$

34. $h = \pm \dfrac{d}{2} (e^{M/k} - 1)^{1/2}$

35. $x = 12$ or -3; $y = 12$ or 2

36. (a) $a = \pm \frac{2}{3}, b = \pm 1\frac{2}{3}, c = \pm 1$

EXERCISE 8.1

4. (a) $(1, \sqrt{3})$ (b) $(-5/2, 5\sqrt{3}/2)$

    (c) $(0, -3)$ (d) $(-2\sqrt{3}, -2)$

(e) $(3\sqrt{3}, -3)$

(f) $(-\sqrt{3}, -1)$

(g) $(4\sqrt{3}, 4)$

(h) $(12, 0)$

(i) $(-\sqrt{3}/2, 1/2)$

(j) $(0, -3)$

5. (a) $[5, \tan^{-1}(4/3)]$

(b) $[13, \tan^{-1}(12/5)]$

(c) $[\sqrt{29}, \tan^{-1}(-5/2)]$

(d) $[\sqrt{45}, \tan^{-1}(-1/2)]$

(e) $[\sqrt{2}, \tan^{-1} 1]$

(f) $[25, \tan^{-1}(-24/7)]$

(g) $[10\sqrt{2}, \tan^{-1}(-1)]$

(h) $[4\sqrt{2}, \tan^{-1} 1]$

(i) $[\sqrt{5}, \tan^{-1}(\sqrt{3}/\sqrt{2})]$

(j) $[\sqrt{13}, \tan^{-1}(\sqrt{8}/\sqrt{5})]$

6. (a) $4r = \sec\theta\tan\theta$

(b) $r = \sec\theta(6 - \tan\theta)$

(c) $r^2 = 16$

(d) $r = 6\cos\theta$

(e) $r^2 = \dfrac{8}{\sin 2\theta}$

(f) $r = \dfrac{2}{8\cos\theta - \sin\theta}$

(g) $r^2 = \dfrac{144}{16\cos^2\theta + 9\sin^2\theta}$

(h) $r^2\sin 2\theta + 4r\sin\theta - 20 = 0$

(i) $4r = \operatorname{cosec}\theta\cot\theta$

(j) $r^2 = \dfrac{\tan^2\theta + 4}{\cos^2\theta}$

7. (a) $x^2 + (y - 1)^2 = 1$

(b) $y = 2$

(c) $x^2 + y^2 = 16$

(d) $y = x\sqrt{3}$

(e) $x^2 + y^2 = 6\sqrt{(x^2 + y^2)} + 6x$

(f) $24xy = (x^2 + y^2)^{3/2}$

(g) $(x^2 + y^2)^2 = 4(x^2 + y^2) - 8y^2$

8. $9\pi/4$

10. Parabola

11. $A = 0.484$; Mean $= 0.308$

12. $\dfrac{\pi}{4}$ to $\dfrac{3\pi}{4}$ and $\dfrac{5\pi}{4}$ to $\dfrac{7\pi}{4}$

13. (a) $(x - a)^2 + y^2 = a^2$

EXERCISE 9.1

1. (a) $2\sin(\omega_1 + \omega_2)t\cos(\omega_1 - \omega_2)t$

(b) $2\cos(F + f)\pi t\sin(F - f)\pi t$

(c) $2\cos\left(\dfrac{\omega + \phi}{2}\right)t\cos\left(\dfrac{\omega - \phi}{2}\right)t$

(d) $-2\sin\left(\omega t + \dfrac{\alpha + \phi}{2}\right)\sin\left(\dfrac{\alpha - \phi}{2}\right)$

(e) $2\sin 4\theta\cos 2\theta$

(f) $2\cos 2\omega t\sin\omega t$

(g) $-2 \sin 3\theta \sin \theta$

(h) $2 \cos \dfrac{5\theta}{2} \cos \left(\dfrac{\theta}{2} + \dfrac{\pi}{3} \right)$

(i) $2 \sin 75t \cos 25t$

(j) $2 \cos \dfrac{\pi}{4} \sin \left(\theta - \dfrac{\pi}{4} \right)$

2. (a) $\sin 6\theta + \sin 2\theta$

(b) $\sin 8\omega t - \sin 4\omega t$

(c) $\cos 150t + \cos 50t$

(d) $\cos 10\theta - \cos 6\theta$

(e) $2 \left[\sin 2\omega t + \sin \dfrac{2\pi}{3} \right]$

(f) $\frac{1}{2}[\cos 2\pi(F + f)t + \cos 2\pi(F - f)t]$

(g) $-\frac{1}{2}[\cos (\omega_1 + \omega_2)t - \cos (\omega_1 - \omega_2)t]$

(h) $\frac{1}{4}[\sin 3\theta + \sin (\theta + \pi)]$ (i) $\frac{1}{2}[\cos 90° + \cos 60°]$

(j) $\frac{1}{2}[\sin (3\alpha + 3\beta) - \sin (\alpha - \beta)]$

3. (a) $\dfrac{\sqrt{2}}{2}$

(b) $\dfrac{1 - \sqrt{3} - \sqrt{6}}{2\sqrt{2}}$

4. $\frac{1}{2}[\sin 2\pi(F + f)t + \sin 2\pi(F - f)t]$

5. 0, 60, 90, 120, 180, 240, 270, 300, 360°

6. 0, 90, 180, 270, 360°

7. 74, d.c.; 34, $f = 2\pi/3\omega$; 2, $f = \pi/3\omega$

8. (a) $y_{\text{mean}} = 1\cdot274$; $y_{\text{r.m.s.}} = 1\cdot583$

(b) $y_{\text{mean}} = 1\cdot274$; $y_{\text{r.m.s.}} = 1\cdot581$

9. $\frac{1}{6} \cos 12\omega t + \frac{1}{2} \cos 14\omega t - \frac{1}{2} \cos 16\omega t - \frac{1}{6} \cos 18\omega t$

$f = \pi/6\omega, \pi/7\omega, \pi/8\omega, \pi/9\omega$

10. 0·1327

11. (a) 12·25 A;   (b) 7 V

12. (a) 280;   (b) 0·6

13. (a) 0·3466;   (b) 0·5708

14. 0·816

15. 39·3

16. (a) 1·50;   (b) 1·50

17. $9\pi/4$

18. $\pi/2$

19. 33·0 cm²

20. 34·1π

21. 93·3π cm³

22. 3π

EXERCISE 10.1

2. (a) $7 + 5j$

4. (a) $5 - j$

(b) $-4 + 20j$

(c) $-16 + 30j$

(d) 2

5. (a) $0\cdot1 + 0\cdot8j$

(b) $-0\cdot21 - 0\cdot68j$

(c) $0\cdot6 - 0\cdot8j$

(d) $1\cdot3 - 0\cdot18j$

6. $1 \pm 1\cdot23j$

7. (a) 13·4; 63° 26′

(b) 4·1; 345° 58′

(c) 7·8; 129° 48′

(d) 11·7; 250° 1′

8. $1 \cdot 11 + 0 \cdot 066j$ **9.** $Z = R + j\omega L$

10. $6 + 8j$; $10\ \Omega$; $53°\ 8'$ **11.** $20\ \Omega$; $318\ \mu F$

12. $500 + j4020\ \Omega$; $4050\ \Omega$; $82°\ 54'$

13. $40 - j53\ \Omega$; $66 \cdot 4\ \Omega$; $-52°\ 58'$ **14.** $0 \cdot 008 - j0 \cdot 063$ A

15. $20 + j63\ \Omega$; $50 + j94 \cdot 2\ \Omega$; $15 + j38\ \Omega$

16. $Y = 0 \cdot 02 - j0 \cdot 0096$ S   **17.** $Y = 0 \cdot 0041 + j0 \cdot 0072$ S

18. $Z = 3 \cdot 35 - j0 \cdot 833\ \Omega$ **19.** $Z = 2 \cdot 85 - j3 \cdot 54\ \Omega$

20. $Z = 2 \cdot 94 - j0 \cdot 451\ \Omega$ **21.** $z = 0 \cdot 366 + j1 \cdot 37$

22. $Z = 4 + j15 \cdot 1\ \Omega$
$= 75°\ 9'$ leading

EXERCISE 10.2

1. (a) $4 \cdot 47\ \underline{|63°\ 26'}$ (b) $5\ \underline{|143°\ 8'}$

   (c) $10\ \underline{|306°\ 52'}$ (d) $9 \cdot 43\ \underline{|212°}$

2. (a) $6 \cdot 43 + j7 \cdot 66$ (b) $-5 \cdot 14 + j6 \cdot 13$
   (c) $-3 \cdot 06 - j2 \cdot 57$ (d) $4 \cdot 46 - j4 \cdot 01$

3. (a) $-38 + j46$ (b) $59 \cdot 7\ \underline{|129°\ 34'}$

4. (a) $45\ \underline{|120°}$ (b) $-22 \cdot 5 + j39$

5. $1 \cdot 47\ \underline{|310°\ 17'}$

6. (a) $4\ \underline{|84°}$;   (b) $1 \cdot 41\ \underline{|21°}$ or $1 \cdot 41\ \underline{|201°}$

7. (a) $-14 + j11$; (b) $-1 - j2$; $\sqrt{5}\ \underline{|243°\ 26'}$

8. $0 \cdot 276\ \underline{|33°\ 38'}$; $13\ \underline{|292°\ 37'}$

9. $Z_0 = 731 - j188$ or $Z_0 = 755\ \underline{|345°\ 35'}$

10. (a) $-3 \cdot 5 + j0 \cdot 5$

   (b) $\sqrt{(R^2 + \omega^2 L^2)}\ \underline{|\theta_1}$ where $\tan^{-1} \theta_1 = \dfrac{\omega L}{R}$

   $\sqrt{(G^2 + \omega^2 C^2)}\ \underline{|\theta_2}$ where $\tan^{-1} \theta_2 = \dfrac{\omega C}{G}$

   $Z_0 = \sqrt[4]{\left(\dfrac{R^2 + \omega^2 L^2}{G^2 + \omega^2 C^2}\right)}\ \underline{\left|\dfrac{\theta_1 - \theta_2}{2}\right.}$; Z_0 real if $\theta_1 = \theta_2$

11. (b) $0 \cdot 7453\ \underline{|296°\ 34'}$; $\frac{1}{3} - j\frac{2}{3}$ (c) $0 \cdot 707 + j2 \cdot 12$; $-0 \cdot 707 - j2 \cdot 12$

12. (b) (i) $0 \cdot 0104 - j0 \cdot 1243$
     (ii) $13\ \underline{|112°\ 37'}$; $169\ \underline{|225°\ 14'}$

13. (a) $0 \cdot 16$ S   (b) $0 \cdot 08$ S
   (c) $0 \cdot 18$ S   (d) $1 \cdot 27$ mF

14. $0 \cdot 01$; $0 \cdot 03$

Index

Printed and bound by McGraw-Hill Far Eastern Publishers (S) Ltd. — Singapore